Inclu:

CW00801502

Edited by:
John Clarkson
Roger Coleman
Ian Hosking
Sam Waller

© 2007 i~design

Printed and bound by Kall Kwik Cambridge
E-mail: info@kkcambs.co.uk
Web: kallkwik.co.uk/cambridge

First published in 2007 by

Engineering Design Centre
Department of Engineering
University of Cambridge
Trumpington street
Cambridge
CB2 1PZ
UK

E-mail: edc-enquiries@eng.cam.ac.uk
Web: www-edc.eng.cam.ac.uk

All rights reserved. No part of this publication may be reproduced in any material form, or stored by any electronic medium without the prior written consent of the copyright holders (except in accordance with the provisions of the Copyright Designs and Patents Act 1988). Applications for the copyright holders written permission to reproduce any part of this publication should be addressed to the publishers.

Front cover image by Susannah Clarke. The shampoo and conditioner bottles use a strong colour contrast and a tactile surface to make differentiation easy for the user, yet this is achieved without any aesthetic compromise.

ISBN 978-0-954243-2-6

Inclusive design
toolkit

If you would like to obtain a large print
version of this book, please contact
edc-enquiries@eng.cam.ac.uk

www.inclusivedesigntoolkit.com

Acknowledgements

This book was produced by Sam Waller. The content was written and edited by: Carlos Cardoso, Susannah Clarke, John Clarkson, Roger Coleman, Joy Goodman, Ian Hosking, Pat Langdon, Umesh Persad, Kay Sinclair, Sam Waller, and Matthew White.

The authors are grateful to all those who helped assist the toolkit production, in particular: Alex Carmichael, Bruce Carse, Julia Cassim, Hua Dong, Diane Douglas, Tim Lewis, Ana Medeiros, Andrew Monk, Nick Reddall, and Tom Vavik.

The authors are grateful to Scope for initiating the Centre for Inclusive Technology and Design awareness and training project; which inspired this toolkit. Please see the About us section in www.inclusivedesigntoolkit.com for more details.

Foreword

Welcome to the Inclusive design toolkit, commissioned by BT and developed in partnership with the i~design research team.

Working with

We live in an increasingly complex and technologically rich world, and can all cite examples of products that are difficult or frustrating to use. By applying inclusive design principles, involving users in the design, and considering the needs of people with reduced capabilities, products can be made usable, useful and desirable.

The Engineering Design Centre, University of Cambridge
www-edc.eng.cam.ac.uk

Sagentia
www.sagentia.com

Royal College of Art, Helen Hamlyn Centre
www.hhc.rca.ac.uk

Centre for Usable Home Technology, University of York www.cuhtec.org.uk

Applied computing, University of Dundee
www.computing.dundee.ac.uk

Preface

This toolkit was written by the Cambridge Engineering Design Centre, together with Sagentia and the Helen Hamlyn Centre. The guidance and resources contained within reflect the outcome from i~design 2, an on-going collaborative research programme on inclusive design funded by the Engineering and Physical Sciences Research Council. The i~design 2 team brings together leading researchers from the Engineering Design Centre, University of Cambridge, Sagentia, Royal College of Art, Helen Hamlyn Centre, Centre for Usable Home Technology, and Appplied computing, University of Dundee.

The creation of the inclusive design toolkit was commissioned and supported by BT as part of their Betterworld initiative.

Working with

BT
www.btplc.com/betterworld

Contents

This toolkit has been developed to explain what inclusive design is, why it is worthwhile and how to do it.

The book is split into four sections, where each section is intended to be self contained, as is each double page spread. In this toolkit, a 'product' refers to the output of design activity, examples of which include consumer products, designer graphics, or the provision of a service.

Part 1: Introduction, explains what inclusive design is, why it is worthwhile, and what corporate level strategy is required to encourage it. Part 2: Inclusive design process examines how the knowledge and tools of inclusive design fit together with a generic design process. Part 3: Knowledge & tools considers these tools in detail. Finally, Part 4: User capabilities provides detailed information on the prevalence of capability within the population of Great Britain, along with design guidance for how the capability demands of a product can be reduced without compromising performance.

Part 1:
Introduction

Part 2:
Inclusive design process

Part 3:
Knowledge & tools

Part 4:
User capabilities

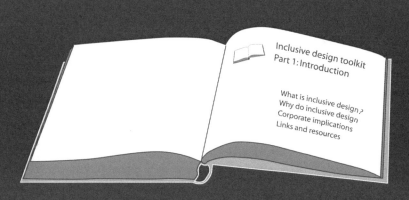

Inclusive design toolkit
Part 1: Introduction

What is inclusive design?
Why do inclusive design
Corporate implications
Links and resources

Part 1:
Introduction

**Roger Coleman, John Clarkson, Joy Goodman
Ian Hosking, Kay Sinclair, and Sam Waller**

Introduction

" Questions about whether design is necessary or affordable are quite beside the point: **design is inevitable.** "

- Douglas Martin (Book Design 1989)

Inclusive design is a methodology that applies throughout the design and development process. It results in better designed products that are more usable and desirable.

Contents

Introduction

What is inclusive design?

Overview

It is important to understand the terms design and inclusive design, the ethos behind inclusive design, and the way inclusive design contributes to product success. A number of case studies demonstrate how inclusive design can foster innovation and better design.

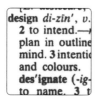 **Definitions of design**

 **Definitions of inclusive design**

 **Ethos of inclusive design**

 **What is needed?**

 **Examples**

Definitions of design

The process of design may be described as

" Design ... to form or conceive in the mind, invent ... "

- Oxford English Dictionary (2005)

" Design is a structured creative process ... All products and services are, in effect, 'designed', even if not by a professional designer. "

- Department of Trade and Industry (2005)

" Design is the purposive application of creativity to all the activities necessary to bring ideas into use either as product (service) or process innovations. "

- Bessant (2005)

" The configuration of materials, elements and components that give a product its particular attributes of performance, appearance, ease of use, method of manufacture. "

- Walsh (1992)

" Design is the process of converting an idea or market need into the detailed information from which a product or system can be made. "

- Royal Academy of Engineering (2005)

" Design ... to form or conceive in the mind, invent ..." (OED, 2005)

Oxford English Dictionary (2005) Oxford University Press, Oxford, UK.
Department of trade and industry (2005) Economics paper 15:
Creativity, design and business performance. Avail. from www.dti.gov.uk
Bessant J, Whyte J, Neely A (2005) Management of creativity and
design within the firm. Advanced Institute for Management and Imperial
College, UK.
Walsh V, Roy R, Bruce M, Potter S (1992) Winning by design. Blackwell
Business, Oxford, UK.
Royal Academy of Engineering (2005) Educating engineers in design.
Avail. from www.raeng.org.uk

Definitions of inclusive design

The British Standards Institute (2005) definition of inclusive design is

" The design of **mainstream** products and/or services that are accessible to, and **usable** by, **as many people** as reasonably possible … without the need for special adaptation or specialised design. "

By meeting the needs of those who are excluded from product use, inclusive design improves product experience across a broad range of users. Put simply **inclusive design** is **better design**.

Inclusive design is not

- Simply a stage that can be added in the design process

- Adequately covered by a requirement that the product should be easy to use

- Solely about designing products for a particular capability loss

- Naively implying that it is always possible (or appropriate) to design one product to address the needs of the entire population

Inclusive design should be embedded within the design and development process, resulting in better designed mainstream products that are desirable to own and satisfying to use.

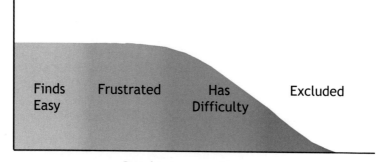

Users

Finds Easy

Frustrated

Has Difficulty

Excluded

Product experience

Philips (2004) found that about two thirds of the population
as a whole have difficulties with technological products

Attempting to open this plastic welded packaging proved to be
impossible by hand, so this user tried more drastic measures

British Standards Institute (2005) British Standard 7000-6:2005. Design
management systems - Managing inclusive design - Guide
Philips (2004) The USA Philips Index: Calibrating the Convergence of
Healthcare, Lifestyle and Technology. A web-based survey of 1500 internet
users aged 18-75, www.usa.philips.com

Ethos of inclusive design

User centred

People within the population have a range of different capabilities and skills, past experiences, wants and opinions. Many organisations already carry out market and user research. Commissioning such research at the right time, with the right focus and within an appropriate design framework enables valuable insight at little, if any, additional cost.

Population aware

A typical misguided viewpoint is that someone is either disabled or fully able, yet a wide spectrum of capabilities is clearly apparent within any population. An understanding of quantitative population statistics can also inform design decisions.

Business focused

Every decision made during the design cycle can affect design inclusion and user satisfaction. Failure to correctly understand the users can result in products that exclude people unnecessarily and leave many more frustrated, leading to downstream problems, such as increased customer support requirements that can ultimately reduce commercial success. Conversely, successful implementation of inclusive design can result in a product that is functional, usable, desirable, and ultimately profitable.

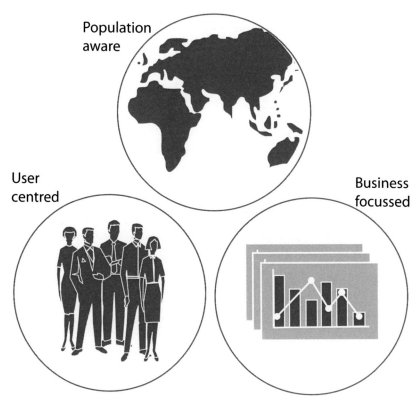

Population aware

User centred

Business focussed

Ethos of inclusive design

What is needed?

Functional
The product must provide suitable features to satisfy the needs and desires of the intended users. A product with a large number of features is not guaranteed to be functional!

Usable
Easy to operate products are pleasurable and satisfying to use, while those that place unnecessarily high demands on the user will cause frustration for many people and exclude some altogether. Frustration with, or inability to use, a product can lead to a negative brand image. In the extreme, prolonged difficulties with poorly designed everyday products can even convince people that they are no longer able to lead an independent life.

Desirable
A product may be desirable for many reasons, including being aesthetically striking or pleasant to touch, conferring social status, or providing a positive impact on quality of life.

Viable
The business success of a product can be measured by its profitability. This typically results from having a product that is functional, usable, and desirable, and which is delivered to the market at the right time and at the right cost.

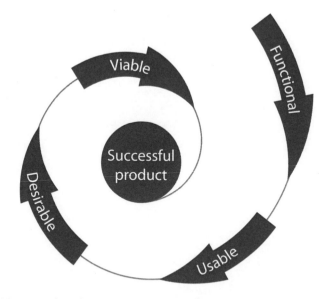

Measures by which a product could be considered successful

Examples: B & Q and Tesco

B & Q: Pressure washers

A collaboration between the Helen Hamlyn Centre and B & Q looked at garden power tools. User research revealed a problem with posture for some people using pressure washers. The researchers, now with Sprout Design, developed a new product concept that is held like a broom instead of a gun, improving posture, control and reach dramatically. The concept also incorporates a new connector for attaching different nozzles, placing significantly less physical, sensory and cognitive demands on the user.

Tesco

Tesco is the UK's biggest private sector employer, and has developed a highly profitable web business, tesco.com, which is the world's largest home shopping service. The web business posted a profit of £12.2 million in 2002-3, an increase of more than 30 times the previous year and a rare example of a profitable dot-com business.

One early innovation was an easy-access version of the site, specifically designed for use with screen readers and slow internet connections. This facility has now been integrated into the main site, as a selectable setting within the user's account.

A pressure washer that has a high physical demand, compared to a redesigned product that reduces the physical strain required to use it

The Tesco food and drink department, viewed with and without selecting the "Use access site" option within "My account"

Top images copyright Helen Hamlyn Centre and B & Q

Examples: OXO Good Grips

OXO began with a few simple questions - Why do ordinary kitchen tools hurt your hands? Why can't there be wonderfully comfortable tools that are easy to use?

In 1990, the first group of 15 OXO Good Grips kitchen tools was introduced to the US market. These ergonomically designed, transgenerational tools set a new standard for the industry and raised the bar of consumer expectation for comfort and performance.

The annual growth in sales was over 35% per year from 1991 to 2002, and the line now contains more than 500 innovative products covering many areas of the home. The OXO Good Grips line has been recognized by several national and international organizations for superior design. The company's strategy is based on the primary goals of making products that are usable and desirable.

See www.oxo.com for more information

The handles on these products have innovative designs that make them comfortable to use, and the blades are functionally very effective

This salad spinner requires minimal capability to use, while this jug has a diagonal measuring scale that can be read from above

Why do inclusive design?

?

Overview

The primary focus of the majority of new product development projects is time and budget. However, delivering the most commercially successful product can conflict with this focus.

There is often the perception that good design takes longer and costs more than bad design. Indeed that design is something we can choose not to do and thereby reduce cost and timescales. In reality, the true costs of bad design (such as warranty returns from unsatisfied customers) emerge later on in the product lifecycle, and have the potential to cause irreparable damage to the brand image through customer frustration.

The following pages aim to demonstrate that an inclusive design approach results in better products with greater user satisfaction and greater commercial success whilst reducing product development risk.

The worldwide case

The company case

The project case

The worldwide case: Age variation

The demographics of the developed world are changing; longer life expectancies and a reduced birth rate are resulting in an increased proportion of older people within the adult population.

This is leading to a reduction in the Potential Support Ratio (PSR), which is the number of people aged 15-64 who could support one person aged over 65.

- In 1950 the worldwide PSR was 12:1

- In 2000 the PSR was 9:1

- By 2050 it will be 4:1 globally and 2:1 in the developed world

Maintaining quality of life and independent living for this ageing population is increasingly important and will soon be an absolute necessity for all countries in both the developed and developing world.

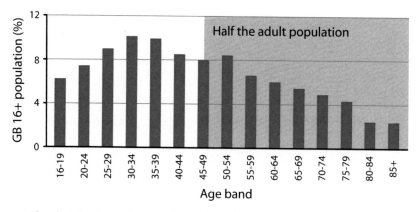

The distribution of age within the adult population of Great Britain

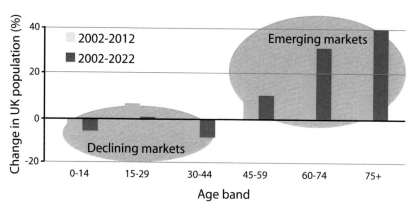

Change in the population within each age band over time

Top figure source: The Disability Follow-up Survey (Grundy et al. 1999)
Bottom figure source: The Government Actuary's Department

The worldwide case: Capability variation

With increasing age comes a decline in capability, yet also increased wealth and free time. Where previous generations accepted that capability loss and an inability to use products and services came hand in hand, the baby-boomer generation now approaching retirement are less likely to tolerate products that they cannot use, especially if due to unnecessary demands on their capabilities.

Typically, people are viewed as being either able-bodied or disabled, with products being designed for one category or the other. In fact capability varies continuously, and reducing the capability demands of a product results in more people being able to use the product as well as increased satisfaction for those who previously had difficulty.

When the capability demand of a product exceeds that of the user – they can no longer use it. Often this is seen as the person's fault for having a poor memory, reduced strength or imperfect vision; inclusive design places the responsibility with product designers to ensure that the capability levels required to use a product are as low as possible. There are several ways to achieve this goal without compromising the features or aesthetics for the more able population, this will be elaborated in further detail in Part 2: Inclusive design process.

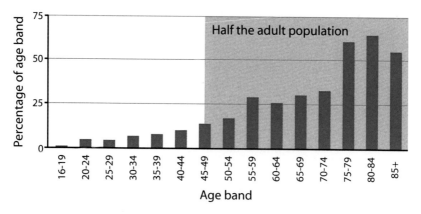

Percentage of people within each age band that have less than full
ability, according to the definition used within Part 4: User capabilities

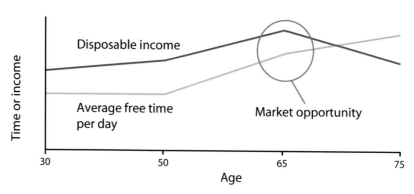

Variation of disposable income and free time with age

Top fig. source: The Disability Follow-up Survey (Grundy et al. 1999)
Bottom fig. source: The Henley Centre, Family Expenditure Survey (1996)

The worldwide case: Simplicity

Ever advancing technology leads to products with ever more features, yet this wealth of features can transfer focus away from a product that is actually useful and usable. Typical household products such as microwaves often have a bewildering array of dials, codes and buttons, so users end up trying to remember the precise action sequence required to achieve one desirable function, and simply ignoring the rest.

The foundation of a successful design is a focus on simplicity, together with an understanding of what users actually want from the product. Philips (2004) found that only 23% of Americans use the full range of features on most new technology products. 65% of Americans say they have lost interest in purchasing a technology product because it seemed too complex to setup or operate. The fact that some products can be set-up and operated easily has raised the bar for what's possible. Ease of use is so important to the public (76%) that it is now equal in importance to the dimension of 'high quality'.

Using technology should not be as frustrating
as trying to eat soup with a fork!

Philips (2004) The USA Philips Index: Calibrating the Convergence
of Healthcare, Lifestyle and Technology. A web-based survey of 1500
internet users aged 18-75 www.usa.philips.com

The company case

Superior company performance

The key test of the value of design from a business perspective is whether a design aware company outperforms its competitors who are not. The Design Council (2005) showed that an index of design aware companies outperformed the FTSE All share by over 200% in both bull and bear markets over a 10 year period.

There are clearly other indicators of good management apart from design, however, the evidence that 'good design is good business' is compelling.

Corporate level risk management

Design is not optional. It is an inevitable consequence of specifying or developing a product or service. The question is whether your design is good, bad or indifferent. Good design helps to manage development risk, asking

- Are you building the right products (or services)?

- Are you building the product right?

These two questions are fundamental to understanding and mitigating risk. It is imperative that the business at a strategic level empowers those developing and managing products to use design effectively to reap the benefit at a corporate level. See the Corporate implications section for more detail on this issue.

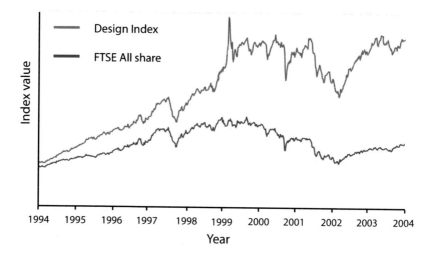

The Design Council (2005) showed that an index of design aware companies outperformed the FTSE All share by over 200% in both bull and bear markets over a 10 year period

" Good design is not simply about aesthetics or making a product easier to use ... it's an essential part of the business. "

- Tony Blair

Design council (2005) Design Index: The impact of design on stock market performance. Available from www.design-council.org.uk Image copyright Design Council, adapted with permission.

The project case

Good design brings a number of benefits to a project.

- Project teams have a clear focus and objective

- Design decisions are made in an informed and decisive manner, without relying on the project team's 'best guess'

The cost of change increases exponentially throughout the design and development lifecycle; hence these costs can be minimised by ensuring a thorough understanding of the real user and business needs at the start of the design process, and correctly translating these needs into an appropriate requirements specification.

Design decisions based on appropriate insight into user needs are likely to carry less risk, and ultimately lead to

- Clear differentiation from the competition

- Customer satisfaction and loyalty

- Market success

Design stage	Relative cost of change
Concept	1
Detail design	10
Tooling	100
Testing	1000
Post-release	10000

The cost of making changes accelerates rapidly as release approaches

Figure source: Mynott C et al (1994) Successful product development: Management case studies. M90s Publications, London

Corporate implication

Overview

A desire to implement inclusive design at a project or product level is often hampered (or stopped) by corporate level issues. In order for genuine and repeatable success to be realised at a project level, there are likely to be a number of implications for the business.

The SPROC (Strategy, Process, Resources, Organisation, and Culture) model considers issues that are key to a business' ability to deliver inclusive design. It is used here to show how senior-level buy-in and support can affect strategic and organisational change that will ultimately cascade down to change at the tactical/project level.

It is unlikely that one product can fit all, but successful management of a product portfolio can be an excellent means to deliver inclusive design.

The SPROC model

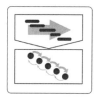

What change may be required?

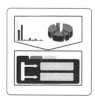

Product strategy

The SPROC model

Inclusive design can be encouraged by considering the SPROC (Strategy, Process, Resources, Organisation, and Culture) model. It is a simple way to represent the elements of a business that can have an impact on its ability to implement inclusive design.

Strategy: Does the high-level business strategy support and encourage inclusive design?

Process: Do existing innovation and development processes incorporate inclusive design considerations. If so, do they function well?

Resources: Does the organisation recognise what resources (internal or external) are required to successfully deliver inclusive design?

Organisation: Do organisational structures, reward systems, and metrics encourage the behaviours required for effective implementation of inclusive design?

Culture: Does the combination of organisational structure, staffing, task design and internal brand values provide for the desire and capability to deliver inclusive design?

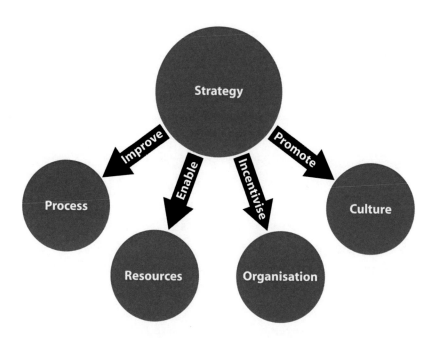

To implement inclusive design, it is necessary to have a strategy that improves the design process, enables sufficient resources, incentivises the organisation, and promotes the right culture

What change may be required?

When senior business management have accepted the value of inclusive design principles and outputs, they are well placed to affect change at the strategic and organisational levels. Of greatest value is their ability to form a strong link between business strategy and inclusive design.

Management support is also required to prevent too narrow a focus on time and budget as measures of development project success. This can inhibit consideration of downstream problems and their associated costs during the earlier parts of the design process, when changes can most easily be implemented. Examples of such costs include no-fault found warranty returns, and customer support.

Without senior support, buy-in and action, the successful delivery of inclusive design is likely to rely on local champions in the business, who actively change approaches within their sphere of influence.

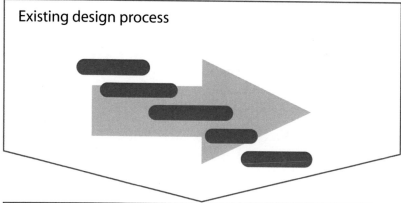

Existing design process

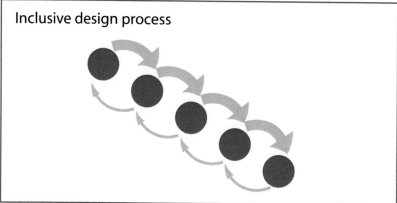

Inclusive design process

An effective inclusive design process can be
built upon an existing design process

Product strategy

Satisfying a range of different users or markets can often be achieved by developing a corresponding range of products in the form of platforms and portfolios. One product may not fit all, but many products can.

Companies need to manage their portfolios to ensure that the range of products and associated feature sets offered matches the spread of capabilities amongst their chosen target population.

For any particular product or feature set, the principles of inclusive design can help to extend the potential market by ensuring that features are intuitive, easy to learn and satisfying to use, without compromising the desirability for the original market. Tools that can be used to manage the overall product strategy include

- Portfolio management

- Product and technology platforms

- Style guides

For more detail on each of these, see the Product strategy section within Part 3: Knowledge & tools.

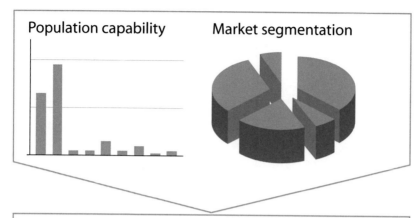

Population capability

Market segmentation

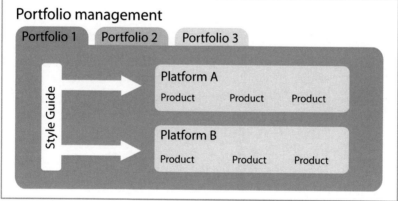

Portfolio management

Portfolio 1   Portfolio 2   Portfolio 3

Style Guide

Platform A

Product   Product   Product

Platform B

Product   Product   Product

Knowledge of population capability statistics and careful analysis of market segments can help to provide targets for specific products, and manage these products using platforms and portfolios

Useful resources

Overview

This section contains references that may be useful to provide further information. They are grouped into categories that loosely correspond with the sections of this toolkit.

- General resources highlights books, websites and conferences relevant to inclusive design

- Training resources indicates participative activities where you can learn more about inclusive design

- Sensory resources are useful to find out more about vision and hearing

- Cognitive resources are useful to find out more about thinking and communication

- Motor resources are useful to find out more about locomotion, reach & stretch, and dexterity

The Design Council's inclusive design website
www.designcouncil.org.uk

General resources: Books

Card SK, Moran TP, Newell A (1983)

The psychology of human-computer interaction. Lawrence Erlbaum Associates, Hillsdale, NJ, USA

Applying psychology to design to make interfaces that are easy, error-free and enjoyable.

Martin J, Meltzer H, Elliot D (1988)

The prevalence of disability among adults. Her Majesty's Stationery Office. ISBN 0-11-691229-4

Report summarising the results from the 1986/87 survey of disability in Great Britain. Contains descriptions of the scales that are used to measure ability/disability in this toolkit.

Grundy E, Ahlburg D, Ali M, Breeze E, Sloggett A (1999)

Research report 94 - Disability in Great Britain. Corporate Document Services, London, UK. ISBN 1-84123-119-3

Report summarising the results from the 1996/97 disability follow-up to the family resources survey, the statistics from which are used throughout this toolkit.

British Standards Institute (2005)

British Standard 7000-6:2005. Design management systems - Managing inclusive design - Guide

Guide to managing inclusive design at the organisational and project levels.

Keates S, Clarkson J (2003)
Countering design exclusion: An introduction to inclusive design. Springer, London, UK
An introduction to designing more inclusive products.

Clarkson J, Coleman R, Keates S, Lebbon C (eds) (2003)
Inclusive design. Springer-Verlag, London, UK
The business case and design toolkit for inclusive design.

Preiser W and Ostroff E (eds) (2000)
Universal Design Handbook. McGraw Hill, New York, USA
A comprehensive academic reference book.

Pirkl JJ (1994)
Transgenerational design. Van Nostrand Reinhold, New York, USA
Examples of age-friendly products.

Coleman R (2001)
Living Longer. Design Council, London, UK
An introduction to the context of inclusive design.

Story MF, Mueller JL, and Mace RL (1998)
The Universal Design File. The Center for Universal Design, NC State University, North Carolina, USA
A guide for studying and evaluating universal design.

General resources: Websites

Design Council About: Inclusive Design

www.designcouncil.org/

A comprehensive knowledge-base covering key aspects of inclusive design.

Helen Hamlyn Centre

www.hhc.rca.ac.uk/index.html

Projects and case studies of inclusive design.

Cambridge Engineering Design Centre

www.eng.cam.ac.uk/inclusivedesign/

Online tutorial.

The US Census Bureau (2006)

www.census.gov

Population statistics.

Trace Research and Development Center

trace.wisc.edu/

Guidelines and resources, focusing on Information and Communication Technology products.

The Adaptive Environments

www.adaptenv.org/

A comprehensive, searchable collection of worldwide resources.

Center for Universal Design

www.design.ncsu.edu/cud/

Seven principles of universal design and case studies.

Center for Inclusive Design and Environmental Access

www.ap.buffalo.edu/idea/

Online universal design education resources.

Wiki for inclusive design

wikid.wikispaces.com

A collaborative forum where users can share their views regarding social aspects of inclusive design and technology.

General resources: Conferences

Include

www.hhc.rca.ac.uk

A biennial international conference on inclusive design, hosted by the Helen Hamlyn Centre, Royal College of Art. Proceedings in CD-ROM format and also available online.

Designing for the 21st Century

www.designfor21st.org/

A biennial or triennial international conference on universal design, hosted by the Adaptive Environments. Proceedings in CD-ROM format and also available online.

CWUAAT

rehab-www.eng.cam.ac.uk/cwuaat/

A biennial workshop on Universal Access and Assistive Technology, hosted by the Engineering Design Centre, University of Cambridge. Proceedings in book format.

International Conference for Universal Design

ud2006.iaud.net/

The occasional conference is hosted by the International Association for Universal Design in Japan.

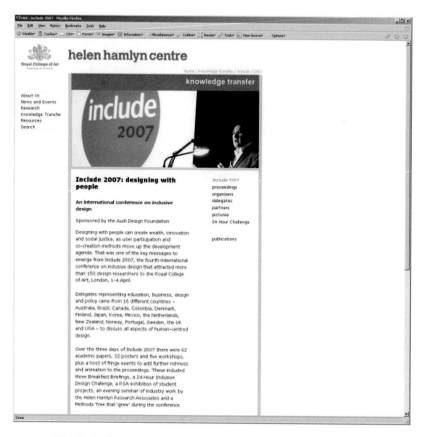

The Include conference provides a unique opportunity for networking with designers, researchers and business leaders

Training resources: Design challenge

The Design Business Association Inclusive design challenge is an annual design competition with a difference. It illustrates the key role design can play in enhancing the quality of life for older and disabled people and all of us.

How does it work? DBA member consultancies from all design disciplines are invited to respond to a design challenge: to create a mainstream product, service, environment or communication, which can be enjoyed equally by consumers of all abilities.

To date, it has resulted in 33 conceptual design projects in inclusive design, involving over 300 designers and been likened to the 'combined Oscars and Olympics of the inclusive design world.'

The success of the annual competition led to the development of a workshop series based on the Challenge model. Workshops of one to three days in duration have been held in the UK, Israel and Japan.

Check out www.hhc.rca.ac.uk/kt/challenge to find out how you can take part.

Example output from a previous design challenge

Training resources: RA Programme

The Research Associates Programme offers an organisation the chance to work on a research, development or communication project of their choice with the Royal College of Art, Helen Hamlyn Centre in London. Projects typically result in new knowledge, products or services that are directly applicable to the host business. Each project lasts for one calendar year, running October to October.

The benefits of participation are best summarised by companies that have joined the Research Associates Programme. They say that participation

- Addresses research and development issues in a way that enhances an organisation's reputation and competitive edge

- Creates tangible design outcomes, including new intellectual property and new knowledge advantageous to the organisation

- Opens up new and surprising creative avenues that can nourish and energise an organisation's design thinking

See www.hhc.rca.ac.uk/research/ra to find out how you can take part

Examples of commercially successful products developed
in collaboration with the RA programme

Sensory resources

Books

Micheal Evamy and Lucienne Roberts (2003)

In sight – a guide to design with low vision in mind.
Rotovision, ISBN: 2880466989

Spotlights exemplar products, environments and graphic information whose development incorporated the input of blind and/or partially sighted people.

Royal National Institue for the Blind (2006)

See it Right – Making information accessible for people with sight problems. RNIB, ISBN: 1858787041. Available from www.rnib.org.uk

Simple guidelines for how to distribute information by print and other formats suitable for people with sight problems.

Websites

Tiresias

www.tiresias.org

In-depth information on assistive devices, research, leg islation and guidelines on accessibility issues focused around visual disabilities.

Lighthouse International

www.lighthouse.org/accessibility/

Guidelines for making text legible and achieving effective colour contrast to suit nearly everyone.

Vision Australia

www.visionaustralia.org.au/info.aspx?page=628

A freeware resource that checks the contrast of colours selected for text and background.

Pfizer Opthalmics

www.visionsimulator.com

Illustrates the changes occurring due to common eye conditions and simulates the effects on a sample image.

Illinois Center for Instructional Technology Accessibility

cita.rehab.uiuc.edu/software/vis/index.php

A simulator capable of applying a number of different visual impairments with variable severity to your computer screen.

Stanford University: Vischeck

www.vischeck.com

Colour blindness simulator for web pages or image files with functionality to improve colour contrast.

Royal National Institute for the Deaf

www.rnid.org.uk/information_resources/

RNID Information Resources.

American Speech-Language Hearing Association

www.asha.org/public/hearing/disorders/types.htm

Description of hearing loss in terms of its type, degree and configuration

Audibel

www.audibel.com/understanding/simulator_flash.html

Hearing loss simulation applied to a single sound sample.

Cognitive resources

Books

Baddeley, A, (2004)
Your memory, A user's guide. Carlton books.

Wickens CD, Hollands JG (2000)
Engineering psychology and human performance, 3rd edition. Prentice-Hall, New Jersey, USA.

Huppert, FA, (2002)
Designing for Older Users, In: J Clarkson, R Coleman, S Keates & C Lebbon (Eds) Inclusive Design: Design for the whole population. Springer Verlag, London, p30-49.

Websites

Afasic: Unlocking Speech and Language:
www.afasic.org.uk/f_speechlang.htm
Information on types and causes of language impairments, aimed primarily at children

Plain English Campaign
www.plainenglish.co.uk
An independent organisation that campaigns against gobbledygook, jargon, and misleading public information. Provides commercial training and editing services.

Royal College of Speech and Language Therapists
www.rcslt.org
Homepage of the professional body for speech and language therapists and support workers.

Salthouse Cognitive Aging Lab (Virginia University)
www.faculty.virginia.edu/cogage
Homepage for research institute on cognitive effects of ageing.

Centre for Speech and Language (Cambridge University)
csl.psychol.cam.ac.uk/
Homepage for speech, language, and brain research centre

Motor resources

Books

Tilley AR (2002)
The Measure of Man and Woman, John Wiley & Sons, New York, USA. ISBN 0-471-09955-4
Gives many physical dimensions for people.

Norris B and Wilson JR (1995)
Childata: The Handbook of Child Measurements and Capabilities. Data For Design Safety, DTI
Detailed anthropometric and strength data for children.

Peebles L, Norris B (1998)
Adultdata: The Handbook of Adult Anthropomorphic and Strength Measurements – Data for Design Safety. Department of Trade and Industry, UK
Detailed anthropometric and strength data for adults.

Smith S, Norris B, Peebles L (2000)
Older Adultdata: The Handbook of Measurements and Capabilities of the Older Adult – Data for Design Safety. Department of Trade and Industry, UK
Detailed anthropometric and strength data for older adults.

Norkin CC and Levangie PK (1992)
Joint Structure & Function: A Comprehensive Analysis. FA Davis, Philadelphia, USA
Function and dysfunction of joints in the human body.

Pheasant S (1987)
Ergonomics - Standards and Guidelines for Designers. British Standards Institution
Draws together ergonomic data from British, European and International standards.

Websites

Better Life Healthcare
www.betterlifehealthcare.com/products.php?catID=6
List of Mobility Aids.

People Size
www.openerg.com/psz.htm
Anthropometric Database.

Department of Trade and Industry
www.dti.gov.uk/files/file21460.pdf
A study of the difficulties disabled people have when using everyday consumer products.

Department of Trade and Industry
www.dti.gov.uk/files/file21811.pdf
Specific anthropometric and strength data for people with dexterity disability.

Inclusive design process

Part 2: Inclusive design process

Roger Coleman, John Clarkson, Ian Hosking
Kay Sinclair, Sam Waller and Matthew White

Contents

Inclusive design process

Inclusive design process

Any product or service is developed by starting from a challenge, captured as a perceived need. Transforming this need into a solution that can successfully satisfy the real need requires an appropriate design process. There are many ways to describe this transformation, but the 'waterfall' model is one of the most useful. It comprises four key stages

- Discover: The systematic exploration of the perceived need to ensure the right design challenge is addressed, with due consideration of all stakeholders; leading to the first output, an understanding of the real need

- Translate: The conversion of this understanding into a categorised, complete and well defined description of the design intent; leading to the second output, a requirements specification

- Create: The creation of preliminary concepts that are evaluated against the requirements; leading to the third output, concepts

- Develop: The detailed design of the final product or service, ready to be manufactured or implemented; leading to the final output, solutions

In addition, evaluation occurs throughout the design cycle.

All decisions made throughout the process affect the level of design exclusion. The objective of this toolkit is to provide the knowledge and tools to minimise the potential for such exclusion.

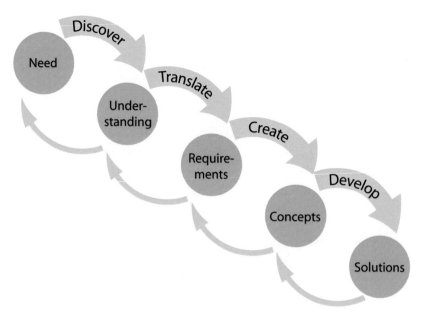

A 'waterfall' model of an inclusive design process

Perceived need: The starting point

A design challenge can arise from a variety of different contexts, such as

- A newly identified market opportunity

- The availability of a new technology

- A requirement to update or repackage an existing product or service

The subsequent discover stage of the product development process encourages exploration of the real needs of all of the relevant stakeholders, leading to an understanding of the true underlying challenge without any implicit prejudice to a particular solution.

This is important as it is often assumed that the perceived need accurately represents the true problem. However, experience shows this is not always the case, it being easy to provide a solution to meet the wrong need. A thorough exploration of the design context will ultimately lead to the identification of the real need.

The exploration of the design context may be enhanced by consulting WikID, a collaborative forum where users can discuss their views on technology wikid.wikispaces.com

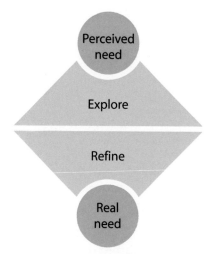

The initial perceived need must be explored and then refined to determine the real need

Perceived need: Example

Back in the 1960's it is said that NASA specified the requirements for a pen capable of writing in zero gravity and spent $1 million dollars developing the 'space pen'; faced with the same problem the Russians took a pencil.

The apparent lesson of this story is a good one, that we can be tempted to spend too much time, effort and money to develop an over-specified solution to a problem, when a perfectly acceptable simple (and cheap?) alternative exists.

The real lesson is rather more subtle. In fact, the pencil was used by both American and Russian astronauts for many years as an effective writing instrument. However, broken leads were a hazard in a zero gravity environment, where they could float into eyes, or equipment causing a short circuit. In addition, pencils (and their leads) would burn rapidly in a pure oxygen environment.

NASA did not at any time specify the requirements for or commission a pen. Paul Fisher, identified the 'real' need for a safer pen and developed the pressurised ball pen, which he presented as a better solution to NASA. The 'space pen' has gone on to be a huge commercial success for Fisher.

This story highlights the importance of exploring the real need; thus identifying the appropriate direction for the design process.

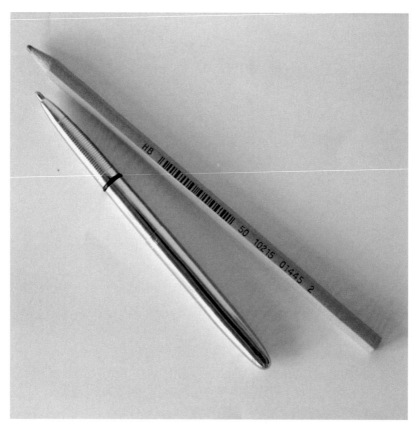

It is said that the Americans developed a space pen for
$1 million dollars, the Russians took a pencil

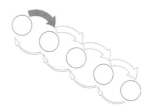

Discover

Good design is about making conscious and well-informed decisions throughout the design process. A great product or service is typically built on a foundation of understanding the real needs of the user and other stakeholders.

Although improving understanding should be an ongoing process, it is initiated at the beginning of the project to discover 'why' are we doing this, and 'what' needs should be addressed.

The focal point of discovery is consideration of the interaction between the user and the potential product or service in its intended use environment. The wider context considers the goals and aspirations of users, together with the tasks they will undertake to achieve these, and the interaction between the business and its product.

The success of a product can be measured in terms of it being functional, usable, desirable and viable, as previously considered in the What is inclusive design? section within Part 1: Introduction. The objective of the discover phase is to build the knowledge foundation to achieve these goals.

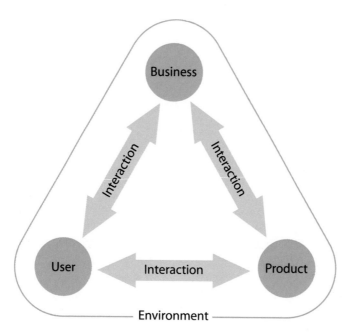

The interactions between user, product and business
all occur within specific environments

Categories for discovery

The discovery process needs to uncover knowledge in response to the following simple questions

- **Who** are the users and other stakeholders?

- **What** tasks will the product be used to achieve?

- **Why** does the business / user want this product?

- **When** will the product be delivered?

- **Where** will the product be used?

The following sections discuss these questions in more detail to ensure the real business and user needs are fully explored

- Users

- Environments

- Scenarios

- Business requirements

The culmination of this discovery process leads to Understanding, to be translated into the requirements detailing how the design team should address the needs.

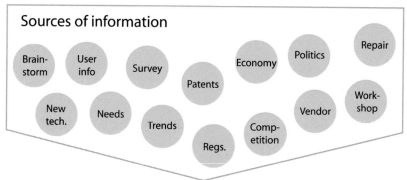

Sources of information

Brain-storm · User info · Survey · Patents · Economy · Politics · Repair · New tech. · Needs · Trends · Regs. · Comp-etition · Vendor · Work-shop

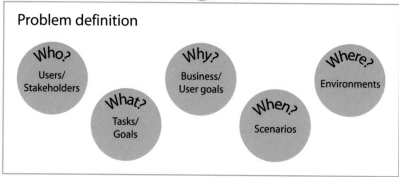

Problem definition

Who? Users/ Stakeholders · What? Tasks/ Goals · Why? Business/ User goals · When? Scenarios · Where? Environments

Aspects that need to be understood

Users: Overview

Do you really know who you are designing for and do you understand them? Does everyone on your team have an accurate and consistent view of who the stakeholders are and how they think?

These questions are relevant in any product development, since there are often other stakeholders, in addition to the users, whose needs must be considered. For example, a toy must satisfy the needs of the child playing with it, as well as the person who purchases the toy.

Understanding the real needs of users and stakeholders provides the foundation for a successful product. For the purposes of this toolkit we are focusing on the users, i.e. the people who attempt to complete a task with the product or service. The following pages explore

- Market segmentation
- Personas
- Product interaction
- Capability losses
- Tasks and goals

Learning about users is a vital aspect of the discovery phase

Users: Market segmentation

There are a number of methods which help to define who the main users are and keep them at the heart of the design and development process.

Market segmentation is one of the key approaches to defining and targeting specific markets. Dividing a market into distinct groups of buyers enables the planning of product mixes, platforms and portfolios to maximise design inclusion.

Effective market segmentation

- **Improves** understanding of the customer base

- **Provides** a clear classification of the customers

- **Enables** the generation of a targeted product portfolio that responds to the needs of the market place

- **Helps** gauge a company's market position relative to the competition

- **Leads** to the effective fine tuning of marketing strategies

Market segments can be brought to life through personas. For further details on market segmentation, see the Categorising users section within Part 3: Knowledge & tools.

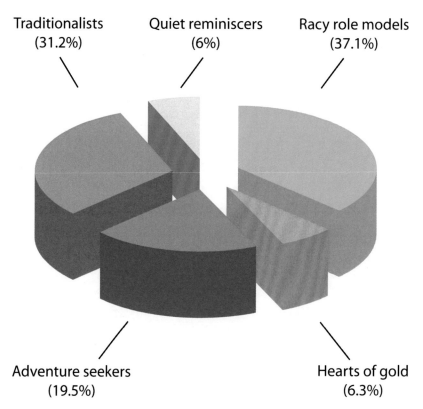

Traditionalists
(31.2%)

Quiet reminiscers
(6%)

Racy role models
(37.1%)

Adventure seekers
(19.5%)

Hearts of gold
(6.3%)

SAGA segmentation of UK grandparents, where a complete
description of each category can be found from
www.saga.co.uk/corporate/press_releases/press_release.asp?id=1543

Users: Personas

Personas represent archetypal users of products and services. Their goals and personal characteristics are indicative of the needs of larger groups of users. They act as

- Substitutes for real users, enabling the project team to stand in their shoes

- Reference points to help guide decisions throughout the design and development programme

Personas aid inclusive design because

- Users' goals and needs become a common point of focus for the team

- The team can design for a manageable set of personas, knowing that they represent the needs of many users

- Design efforts can be prioritised based on the personas

- Disagreements over design decisions can be resolved by referring back to the personas

- Designs can be evaluated against the personas and their capabilities

The successful use of personas is critically dependent upon their relevance to the target market segments, together with the experience and imagination of the design team.

For further details on personas, see the Categorising users section within Part 3: Knowledge & tools.

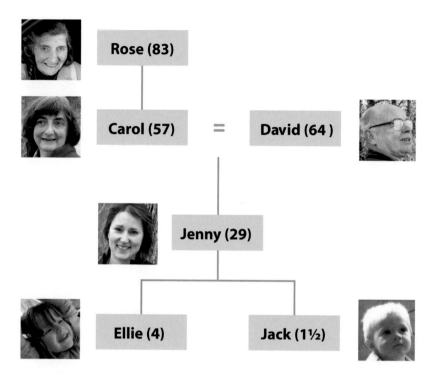

A persona family tree, where each persona is further elaborated within the Categorising users section of Part 3: Knowledge & tools

Users: Product interaction

Any interaction with a product or service typically requires an iterative cycle where the user

- Perceives

- Thinks

- Acts

This cycle can occur very rapidly, where the user perceives information from a product through a range of sensory inputs, chooses and executes a particular action, perceives the resulting change, and so on.

The user's sensory, cognitive, and motor capabilities are used in combination throughout the interaction cycle, with vision and dexterity most often required for perceiving and acting respectively.

The particular environment in which the interaction takes place also significantly influences the user's capabilities. The Framework section within Part 4: User capabilities provides more information on the cycle of product interaction.

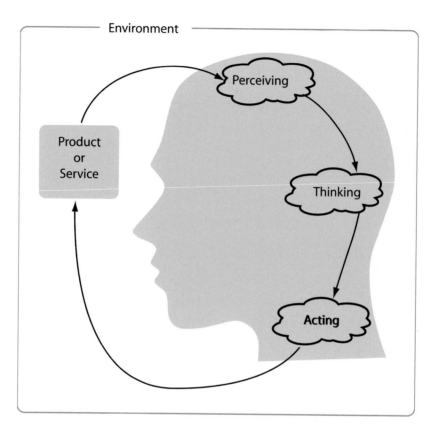

An interaction with a product involves a cycle where the user's capabilities are used to perceive, think and then act

Users: Capability losses

As the cycle of product interaction requires a combination of sensory, cognitive and motor capabilities, it is essential to realise that some people are fully able, while others may be less able in one or more of these capabilities.

Population statistics that consider multiple capability losses can only be calculated if they are generated from a single data set, which is why the statistics from the 1996/97 Disability Follow-up Survey (Grundy 1999) are used throughout this toolkit. In this particular survey, user capabilities are grouped as follows

- **Sensory** capability includes vision and hearing

- **Cognitive** capability includes thinking and communication

- **Motor** capability includes locomotion, reach & stretch and dexterity

According to the definitions used in the Disability Follow-up Survey, 17.8 % of the UK adult population have less than full ability in one or more of these categories. See Part 4: User capabilities for further information on these capabilities, and the precise definition of full ability used in the survey.

Understanding how capability loss occurs, and the relative prevalence of different losses enables the design of products or services that are accessible to the widest possible range of people.

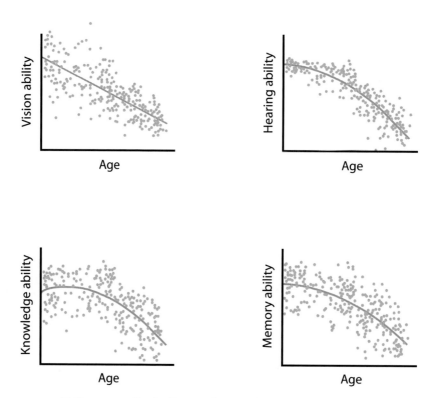

Ability generally declines with age, although consideration
of variation in ability is vital (Adapted from Baltes 1997)

Grundy E, Ahlburg D, Ali M, Breeze E, Sloggett A (1999) Research
report 94 - Disability in Great Britain. Corporate Document Services,
London, UK. ISBN 1-84123-119-3.
Baltes PB and Lindenberger U (1997) Emergence of a powerful
connection between cognitive functions across the adult life span: A new
window to the study of cognitive aging? Psychology and aging v 12 no
1 p12-21. Copyright American Psychological Association. Adapted with
permission.

Users: Tasks and goals

Developing products that are both inclusive and successful requires exploration of tasks and goals to understand the real needs of users.

- **Goals** capture the desires and feelings of the user, for example
    - Enjoying my leisure time
    - Educating my child well
    - Feeling secure when banking online

- **Tasks** are activities that achieve those goals, for example
    - Going on holiday
    - Buying a toy to encourage learning
    - Authenticating your identity on a website by using a password

For more information on how to organise these tasks and goals see the Task analysis section within Part 3: Knowledge & Tools.

A user authenticating her identity on a banking website in order to feel secure when banking online

A couple going on holiday in order to enjoy their leisure time

Environments

Products are used in many different environments that can enhance or hamper the user experience. The impact can be particularly significant for people with reduced capability.

Elements of the social factors include

- **Friends and family** who can share experiences and knowledge to help learn product features

- **A public audience** who can encourage or discourage actions due to peer pressure or humiliation

Elements of the physical factors include

- **Temperature,** which can affect people's temperament, sweatiness, and dexterity

- **Attention,** which can be distracted by environmental factors, resulting in more errors and a difficulty in completing tasks

- **Ambient lighting,** which affects visual performance and causes problems such as glare

- **Background noise** and the acoustic environment can make sounds and speech harder to distinguish

An understanding of the different environments within which a product might be used is a critical element in creating realistic scenarios.

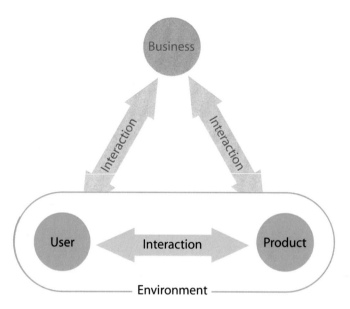

The importance of the environment, in the wider
context of user-product interaction

Scenarios

A scenario represents a context of use; it is a snapshot of a specific user with a certain task and goal in a particular environment.

As products can be used for many different purposes, choosing an appropriate and representative set of scenarios can illustrate the variety of users, environments, goals and tasks the product should be designed for. This helps to

- Provide a focus for the design team

- Highlight usage outside of a product's mainstream purpose

- Ensure the design team considers needs beyond their own immediate experience

Scenarios can highlight usage outside of a product's mainstream purpose

Business requirements: Introduction

When designing a product it is important to be able to answer the fundamental question, 'what constitutes success for the business?'

A well articulated, prioritised and communicated understanding of the business requirements is a prerequisite for making informed design decisions.

Business requirements can be categorised under the following headings

- **Objectives** such as the desired
  - Market share
  - Margins
  - Time to market
  - Return on investment

- **Resources** such as the available
  - Budget
  - Timescales
  - Personnel

- **Corporate fit** such as
  - How does it fit with other products?
  - How does it support the brand?

Objectives	Resources	Fit

- Increase market share by 11%

- Maintain or improve gross margins

- Launch new product by end July 2008

Business requirements can be categorised under the
headings of objectives, resources and corporate fit

Business requirements: Priorities

In reality there will be many business requirements. If effective decision making is to take place, these requirements must be prioritised, particularly where there are conflicts, e.g. between product performance and cost. One simple but effective approach to address such trade-offs is the MoSCoW principle, which stands for

- Must have
- Should have
- Could have
- Won't have

Whilst usability is a key focus for inclusive products, the effective management of conflicting requirements is essential to achieve usability alongside business success. Placing all requirements into the categories above helps to

- Set and communicate priorities
- Encourage buy-in within the project team

Must have

- Gate cost < £35.50
- Prototypes for conference in Feb 2008
- 20,000 units in market by end Q3 2008

Should have

- Capital investment < £500,000
- Market launch by end H1 2008

Could have

- Modular subsystems

Won't have

- Weight > 450g

The MoSCoW model is one simple but effective approach to address conflicts

First output: Understanding real needs

Understanding of the real needs of the users and the business is critical to development of a successful and inclusive product. The project team should now have documented answers to the questions

- **Who** are the users and other stakeholders?

- **What** tasks will the product be used to achieve?

- **Why** does the business / user want this product?

- **When** will the product be delivered?

- **Where** will the product be used?

The project team must also

- Understand what makes the product functional, desirable, profitable and usable

- Understand how these needs may contradict each other

- Prioritise the needs

- Manage and resolve the conflicts between needs

The project team's understanding of the real needs will have significantly improved since the start of the design process and should continue to improve throughout the remaining stages. Subsequent outputs from the design process should be corroborated against this understanding to ensure that any incongruencies are identified and resolved.

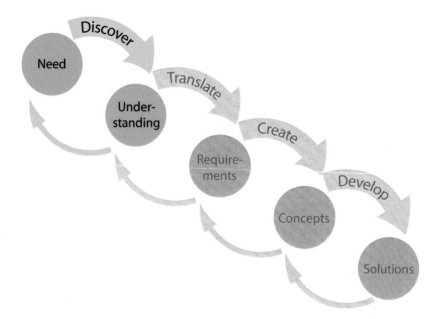

The first output of the design process is an
understanding of the real needs

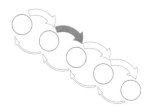

Translate

The **understanding** of real needs gained in the discover stage of the design process now has to be **translated** into a **requirements** specification, which structures the information in an unambiguous form that can be used to develop concepts.

The requirements specification captures the knowledge gained about the users, tasks, and environments; together with the targets for functionality, desirability, profitability and usability.

This translation process will be illustrated with respect to

- Defining tasks and functions
- Lifecycle requirements
- Principles for good requirements
- Structuring the output

The output of the translation process forms the requirements.

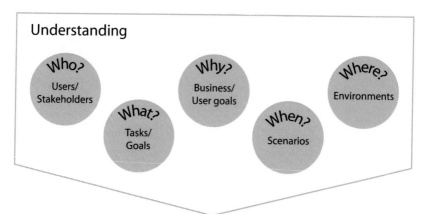

Understanding

Who?
Users/
Stakeholders

What?
Tasks/
Goals

Why?
Business/
User goals

When?
Scenarios

Where?
Environments

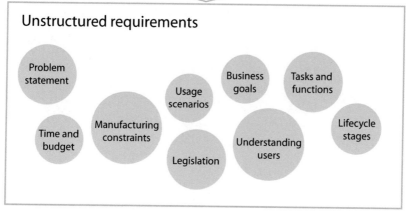

Unstructured requirements

Problem
statement

Usage
scenarios

Business
goals

Tasks and
functions

Time and
budget

Manufacturing
constraints

Legislation

Understanding
users

Lifecycle
stages

The understanding that has been gained now
needs to be translated into requirements

Defining tasks and functions

The translation process begins by gathering detail on the functions that the product needs to perform, as a way of clarifying the interaction between the user and product. It is useful to summarise each function with a verb and noun pair.

Functional analysis comprises

- The definition of a high-level description of the overall function of the product, e.g. 'make a hot drink'

- The decomposition of this high level task into a series of sub-functions, e.g. 'fill heating device', 'heat water', and 'pour water'

- Further expansion of the sub-function descriptions to answer the question 'how?'

- Termination of the process before the descriptions prescribe a specific solution

The functional description can then be expanded to consider the total lifecycle of the product, which may include purchase, installation, use, maintenance, storage, and disposal.

The Task analysis section within Part 3: Knowledge & tools provides further information on this technique.

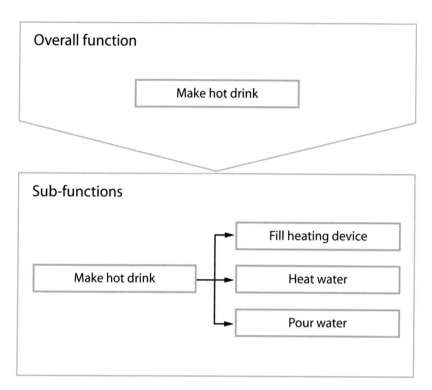

Overall function

Make hot drink

Sub-functions

Make hot drink → Fill heating device
→ Heat water
→ Pour water

A functional analysis starts with a high level description of the overall function, which is then broken down into sub-functions

Lifecycle requirements

A requirements matrix can be used to help ensure that all the necessary requirements have been captured. The matrix combines each of the common requirements headings, with each of the main lifecycle stages of the product.

Common requirement headings

- Performance requirements
- Cost requirements
- Process requirements

Main lifecycle stages

- Design
- Manufacturing and distribution
- Purchasing and set-up
- Usage
- Disposal

	Performance	Cost	Process
Design	Design performance	Design cost	Design process
Manufacturing and distribution	Manufacturing performance	Manufacturing cost	Manufacturing process
Purchasing and set-up	Purchasing performance	Purchasing cost	Purchasing process
Usage	Usage performance	Usage cost	Usage process
Disposal	Disposal performance	Disposal cost	Disposal process

Example of the headings that could be suitable
for requirements specification

Translate

Principles for good requirements

The requirements specification is a document that contains all the constraints that any viable solution should satisfy. These can be categorised into requirements that

- **Must** be satisfied (demand)
- **Should** be satisfied (wish)

The wishes can also be prioritised to help evaluate solutions that satisfy different wishes.

A good requirements specification should be

- **Solution** independent
- **Specific**, **objective**, and **quantified** where possible
- **Measurable** and **testable**
- **Traceable** so that the source of the requirement is understood
- **Accurate** in their representation of the true needs
- **Complete** such that any solution that meets the requirements will be satisfactory
- **Well structured**

Poor Statements	Better Statements
"The product should be easy to use"	"The product should be usable by 95% of adults aged 16-70"
"The maximum opening angle of the car door must be greater than 80 degrees"	"The front seats must be accessible from a wheelchair"

Examples of requirements statements

Translate

The Toyota Porte uses a novel solution for enabling access to the car seats, which might have been overlooked if the specification prescribed a conventional hinged door

Structuring the output

Having defined the tasks and functions, the information needs to be consolidated into an appropriate format. The structured document should capture all of the requirements that a product must satisfy to be successful and inclusive. Critical sections include

- Performance requirements
    - Geometry, forces, weights
    - Aesthetics, finish, colour
    - Usability, including environments and targets for capability demand

- Cost requirements
    - Target material and labour costs

- Process requirements
    - Scheduling and timings
    - Normal use, special use, misuse

A key objective for the document is to ensure that the information is presented in an easily accessible and unambiguous format. The most appropriate headings and sub-categories will ultimately depend on the application being considered.

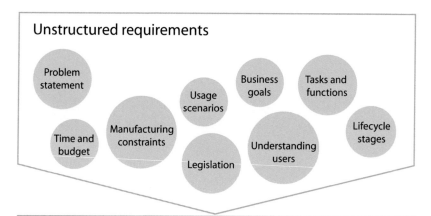

Unstructured requirements

- Problem statement
- Usage scenarios
- Business goals
- Tasks and functions
- Time and budget
- Manufacturing constraints
- Legislation
- Understanding users
- Lifecycle stages

Requirements specification

Cost requirement A

Cost requirement B

Cost requirement C

etc

Performance requirement A

Performance requirement B

Performance requirement C

etc

The requirements specification represents a complete
statement of the design intent, in a structured format

Second output: Requirements

The completed requirements specification should be a clearly defined statement of the design intent, including

- The business requirements that need to be satisfied

- The user needs that must be addressed

The project team should evaluate the specification to ensure it correctly reflects the current understanding of real needs: this understanding may have improved during the translation process.

Throughout the remainder of the design process, further knowledge gained should be used to update and improve the requirements specification. Any changes made should be clearly identified, dated and traceable.

Using the specification to generate design concepts is one way of testing both its validity and clarity. If such concepts satisfy the requirements, but not the real needs, then some aspect of the specification is flawed.

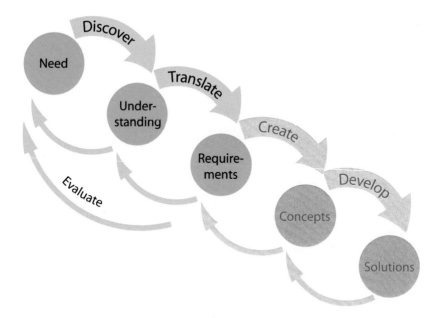

Need

Discover

Under-standing

Translate

Require-ments

Create

Concepts

Develop

Solutions

Evaluate

Translate

The requirements should be evaluated against the underlying needs to ensure they provide an appropriate specification for the design team

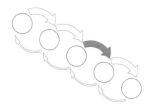

Create

Having identified the requirements that need to be addressed, the next phase of work requires tools and techniques to stimulate a creative process, structure the approach, and then filter and rank the potentially large number of ideas that have been generated.

Team selection is an important part of any project, but particularly in the creative phase where a diverse range of contributors can rapidly deliver a broad range of potential ideas to address a problem.

Ideally the team will be multi-disciplinary, so will include R & D, marketing, manufacturing and so on. This brings a combination of multiple perspectives as well as buy-in from the wider organisation. The key challenge is ensuring that this diverse team can work together in a constructive manner, which may be achieved by selecting key individuals, obtaining senior sponsorship and using effective facilitators in creative sessions.

Appropriate team selection is critical for creativity

Stimulating the creative process

Many organisations have invested in training in the use of creative tools and techniques, a number of which are available and applicable to different situations.

The formation of a design team that is skilled in the broadest range of techniques encourages selection of the right tool for the job. Many tools are well described and freely available online. For example, an internet search for 'creative tools' will provide a plethora of potential sources, including

www.mindtools.com/pages/main/newMN_CT.htm
Tools for developing creative solutions.

www.mycoted.com/Category:Creativity_Techniques
A wiki covering a growing range of creativity and innovation tools and processes.

Involving users or personas with capability losses in creative sessions can provide stimulus for the design team to think in new directions, potentially resulting in solutions that are useful to all users. The Design Business Association Inclusive Design Challenge uses a design model that incorporates real users www.hhc.rca.ac.uk/kt/challenge.

Facilitated group sessions can stimulate creativity

Structuring the output

Of the numerous tools and techniques available, a key subset are those that structure and visualise the creative process and its output. For example

- Mind maps

- Analogy maps

- Lifecycle maps

- Morphological grids

Without these tools, the output of a creative session is too often a list or stack of ideas, with little awareness of what areas have been covered or not.

These tools make it far easier to understand what areas the creative space could cover (guidance for facilitating creative sessions) and what areas have been addressed by idea generation to date.

Using these tools enables the team to ensure they have developed an appropriately large number of ideas. This in turn highlights the next challenge - how to filter and select ideas for further development.

Structuring ideas helps to raise awareness of what has been covered

Filtering and ranking

The creative process can produce very large numbers of ideas for consideration, the sheer volume of which can be daunting. It is therefore important to identify and agree a simple set of criteria, based on the inclusive design intent as captured by the requirements specification, and on acceptable levels of design and business risk.

Filtering and ranking involves

- **Clustering** similar ideas

- **Removal** of all ideas which the team are sure do NOT meet the criteria, or are not technically appropriate

- **Combining** desirable attributes, elements or principles to form a reduced number of improved concepts

- **Ranking** concepts based on fit to the agreed criteria

Initially, when ideas are not well developed, it may be difficult to predict how well they could ultimately satisfy the different criteria. The most pragmatic approach is to use a group of suitable individuals who can provide an educated indication of fit with all of the agreed criteria.

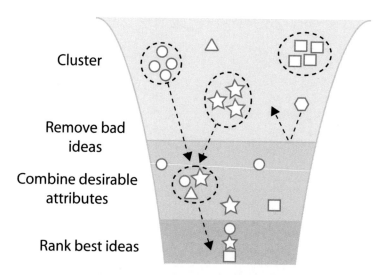

Cluster

Remove bad
ideas

Combine desirable
attributes

Rank best ideas

The process of filtering reduces the number of ideas that are considered,
while allowing their most desirable attributes to combine

Create

Third output: Concepts

In producing a concept, the objective is to demonstrate

- How it can be achieved technically

- The potential look and feel

- The user or market need being addressed

- The value to the business

The first two objectives often involve some form of physical or virtual prototyping, allowing rapid user feedback and validation of the last two. The aim of any prototype created is to get feedback and buy-in from key stakeholders (external and internal), so the best approach(es) to achieve this aim should be chosen.

Prototypes can be evaluated against the design requirements using techniques such as expert appraisal and user testing.

For more explanation of these tools, see the Evaluation tools and Task analysis sections within Part 3: Knowledge & Tools.

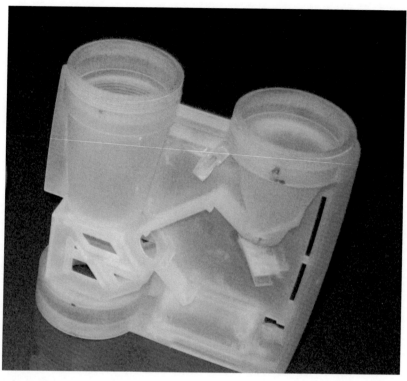

Rapid prototype of a laser rangefinder produced by stereolithography

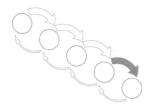

Develop

Further detailed design, manufacturing and marketing activities are required to deliver the solution. Indeed most organisations already have robust, well defined processes for delivering new products to market. Developing inclusively designed products should not require wholesale alteration of these existing approaches.

The key challenge is to deliver the project on time and on budget, without compromising the design intent. In reality, design teams often make numerous small decisions that individually appear to be cost-effective or pragmatic, but in combination erode the product's ability to meet the original inclusive design requirements, therefore reducing its commercial success.

It is essential to quickly identify the barriers that will inevitably impede the development process, such as
- Cost and time restrictions
- Intellectual property issues
- Reluctance of key stakeholders

Decisions to overcome these barriers must be evaluated according to their impact on critical aspects of the requirements specification.

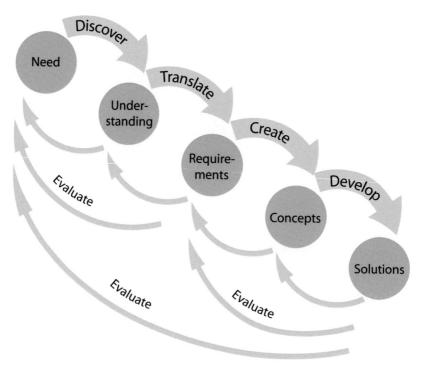

Continuous evaluation is an essential part of a
successful inclusive design process

Final output: Solutions

When the project team develops and delivers a solution, it is imperative to evaluate it against

- The requirements specification (verification)
- The ability to satisfy the real needs (validation)

It is particularly important to evaluate the solution itself, rather than focus on the project performance as measured by development cost and time. Some useful evaluation activities include

- Direct or indirect observation of user interaction with the product
- Measurement of the level of help and support required to use the product
- Monitoring of the incidence of no-fault found returns

User-focused evaluation will help build a picture of product use that has direct relevance to the future commercial success of the product. The insights gained into how customers 'really' use the product may also stimulate new business opportunities, identifying 'needs' that initiate further product development. The 'waterfall' model of the design process may be adapted to reflect this iteration and redrawn as a 'spiral' model.

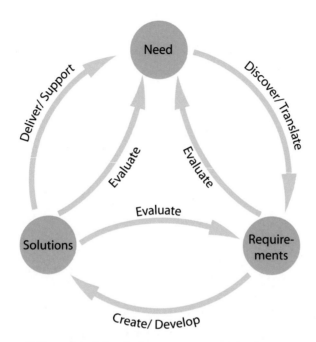

The 'waterfall' model of the design process may also be represented by a 'spiral' model where solutions are delivered in response to the initial need

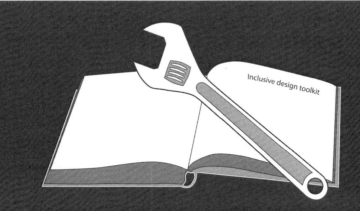

Inclusive design toolkit

Part 3: Knowledge and tools

John Clarkson, Joy Goodman, Ian Hosking

Kay Sinclair, Sam Waller and Matthew White

Knowledge & tools

This section gives a detailed explanation of each of the tools and techniques that have been introduced within Part 2: Inclusive design process.

Contents

Knowledge & tools

Product strategy

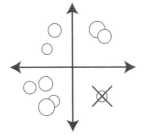

Matthew White and Sam Waller

Overview

A single product will often be unable to address the entire range of different user needs that exist within the potential market. A portfolio of products therefore needs to be developed in order to maximise the customer base without compromising desirability.

Companies need to be able to manage such a portfolio of products and development projects. Platforms provide a mechanism for reducing the number of development projects and increasing returns on development expenditures. In creating a range of products, companies may also use mechanisms such as style guides to ensure an appropriate degree of commonality across the products.

 **Portfolio management**

 **Platforms**

 **Style guides**

Portfolio management

Portfolio management ensures effective resource allocation to meet the short and long-term needs of the organisation. The key goals of portfolio management are to

- Maximise the value of the portfolio

- Ensure a balance between risk and reward

- Ensure strategic alignment within the company

- Match the projects with available resources

In managing a portfolio, one approach to maximising returns and minimising the number of projects being considered is to identify projects that have common needs and can be addressed as platform projects.

This approach can effectively address a variety of user needs, with a range of related products built around a common technology platform. For example, automotive companies use a portfolio approach to provide a variety of performance or styling options to the customer, delivered within the budget of a single product development cycle.

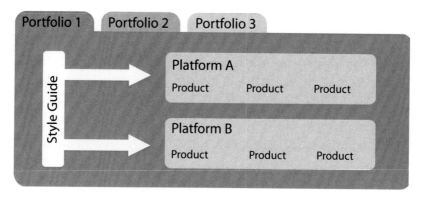

A portfolio contains platforms and style guides, and each
platform can be used to generate multiple products

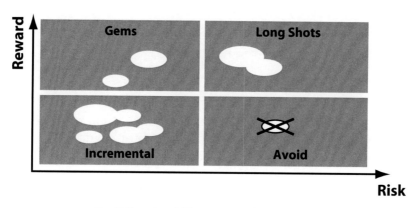

Portfolios should be managed to ensure a
balance between risk and reward

Platforms

Platforms are a way of sharing technology across multiple products, thereby delivering slightly different end-products using the same technical 'template'. Re-using modules, sub-assemblies, or fundamental technologies across multiple products can increase the combined manufacturing volumes, thereby reducing individual costs. Platforms can also enable the development costs for each technology to be spread out over a larger number of products.

Each technology platform can be applied to different product platforms, enabling design skill, experience and lessons learned to transfer across the company.

Within a particular platform, different products can offer a range of feature levels or marketing priorities, in order to match the needs of different market segments.

The different products produced from each platform can be targeted towards different user groups, thereby helping to resolve the inevitable compromise between being functional, usable, and desirable for users with a range of capabilities, whilst remaining viable for the business.

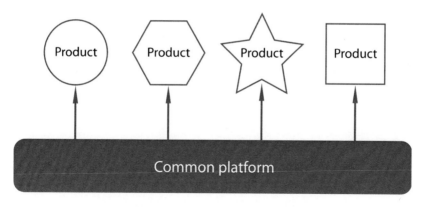

A common platform can be used to generate several products with alternative forms and features

These two shower units were both produced from the same platform

Style guides

Style guides are internal company documents that aid the design process across multiple products and portfolios. They can help to ensure

- Effective reuse of design and understanding across the portfolio
- Consistency of operation (a major contributor to usability)
- Brand compliance

Style guides can be used at different levels to aid compatibility within

- An entire industry
- A particular company
- Portfolios
- Product platforms

These guides are frequently implemented in a web-based or intranet format and can also be called design pattern libraries.

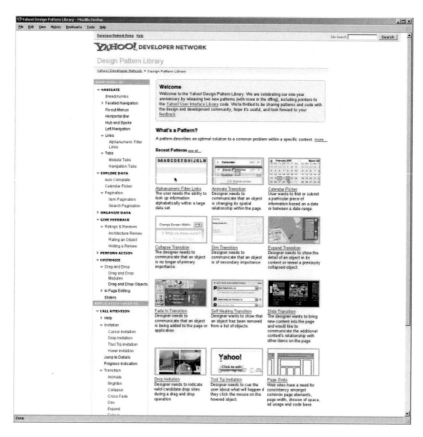

Design pattern library from Yahoo
developer.yahoo.com/ypatterns/

Product strategy

Categorising users

Kay Sinclair and Ian Hosking

Overview

How can a product or service be designed to meet the needs of the intended customers or users? The first step is to classify the market into distinct subsets (segments) that behave in the same way or have similar needs. Customers that fit into a specific market segment should be fairly homogeneous in their needs and attitudes, i.e. they are likely to have similar feelings and ideas about a given product or service, sold at a given price, distributed and promoted in a certain way.

Whilst market segments are very valuable, they are not always easy to visualise. What is needed is a description of one or more individuals that represent that segment, defined in a way that the project team can understand and relate to. These personas are a tool to provide insight into what motivates people to use a product, so that well-grounded decisions can be made about features and how they are presented.

 **Market segmentation**

 **Personas**

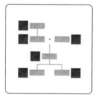 **Example set of personas**

Market segmentation: Introduction

Market segmentation provides a quantitative breakdown of the market, classifying consumers according to a set of factors, which are likely to include

- Demographic factors (age, family size, stage in life, education, occupation)

- Geographic factors (state, region, country)

- Behavioural factors (product knowledge, usage, buying habits, decision making patterns, responses)

- Psychographic factors (lifestyle, attitude, ethnicity, culture, values, personality, approach to risk)

The overall intent is to

- Identify groups of similar potential customers

- Prioritise the groups to address

- Help understand behaviour patterns

- Respond with appropriate strategies that satisfy the different preferences of each chosen segment

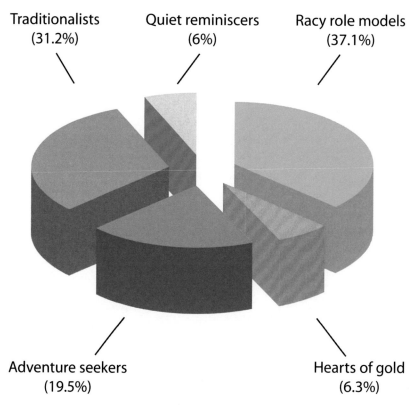

Traditionalists (31.2%) · Quiet reminiscers (6%) · Racy role models (37.1%) · Adventure seekers (19.5%) · Hearts of gold (6.3%)

SAGA segmentation of UK grandparents, where a complete description of each category is available from www.saga.co.uk/corporate/press_releases/press_release.asp?id=1543

Categorisung users

Market segmentation: Useful tips

For effective market segmentation

- The characteristics of people within each segment should be homogeneous

- Each segment should ideally be mutually exclusive

- Segments must be measurable and identifiable

- Segments or target markets should be accessible and actionable to the business

- Each segment must be large enough to provide a solid customer base and hence be profitable

Each segment requires a separate marketing plan

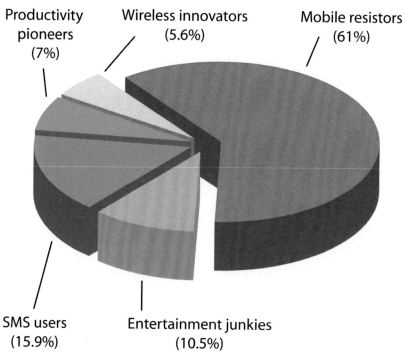

Productivity
pioneers
(7%)

Wireless innovators
(5.6%)

Mobile resistors
(61%)

SMS users
(15.9%)

Entertainment junkies
(10.5%)

IDC segmentation of US wireless users, where a complete
description of each category is available from
www.geekzone.co.nz/content.asp?contentid=754

Categorisung users

Personas: Introduction

Personas provide a qualitative representation of user behaviour and bring users to life by giving them names, personalities and lifestyles. They identify the motivations, expectations, goals, capability, skills and attitudes of users, which are responsible for driving their product purchasing and usage behaviour.

Although personas are fictitious, they are based on the knowledge of real users. Some form of user research is necessary to generate personas that represent real end users, rather than the opinions of the project team.

It's easy to assemble a set of user characteristics and call it a persona, but it's not so easy to create personas that are truly effective tools for design and communication.

For each product or service, it is useful to create a small set of personas to provide a focus for the design team.

Personas can represent the variety of people in the market

Personas: Targets and goals

An obvious, but not necessarily appropriate, persona to use as a design target is the one that brings in the most revenue. To highlight the importance of choosing design targets carefully, consider the following example.

A frequent business traveller would be a tempting target for the design of an in-flight entertainment system. However, this user would be familiar with both flying and computer use. By designing for the business traveller, the retired bricklayer going on holiday may not be able to use the system; yet it is possible to satisfy both personas by designing for the bricklayer, and then assessing the design using the business traveller.

Each persona should have three or four important goals that focus the design. Remember that goals and tasks are different, since tasks are things we do to accomplish goals.

- **Experience goals** describe how a persona wants to feel when using a product, examples include having fun, feeling safe or secure, or not feeling stupid or incompetent

- **Life goals** describe how a persona views the future and are often less useful in design, e.g. 'Retire by age 45' is a valuable insight in designing a financial planning tool, but less useful if you are designing a mobile phone

Ideally, goals should focus on what the persona would get from using a well-designed product or service.

Personas can represent the variety of people in the market

Personas: Useful tips

A good persona description is not a list of tasks or duties; it is a narrative that describes the flow of someone's day, as well as his or her skills, attitudes, environment, and goals. A persona answers critical questions that a task list does not, such as why the persona wants to use the product, and whether they can focus on one thing at a time, or experience lots of interruptions.

It is preferable to keep the number of personas required to illustrate key goals and behaviour patterns to a minimum. There is no magic number, but evidence from experienced and successful designers suggests that between four and eight personas would usually suffice to provide a focus for a single product.

When designing personas, focus first on the information that is critical for design, such as the behaviour patterns, goals, environment, and attitudes of the persona. Then add one or two personal details and facts, such as what your persona does after work. Add life to the persona, by giving a few examples of things that the persona never gets time to do. With a little personality, personas can become useful design targets.

Personas can represent the variety of people in the market

Example set of personas: Introduction

This set of personas was constructed as a training tool. They represent a family of four generations. The important factors to note are

- The variation in capability between the different personas

- The influence of lifestyle and life stages on product use

- The aspirations for each persona, and hence the motives to achieve different tasks with different products

- The position of each persona within a family or social network

Each of these factors will impact on the personas approach to, and interaction with different products. The following personas will now be examined in turn

- Jenny

- Jack and Ellie

- Carol

- David

- Rose

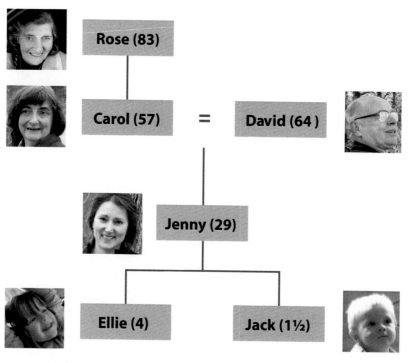

Relations between the members of this persona family

Example set of personas: Jenny

Mother (Age 29)

Jenny is a single mother to Jack and Ellie.

Going shopping as a family is always an adventure. Ellie is curious about everything and often wanders off in a world of her own, unaware of where her mother is, while Jack longs to run around and often tries to escape from his buggy. Two active children, a buggy and bags of shopping do not make for an easy or comfortable bus journey!

Jenny's time is incredibly precious to her and so she has little patience with anything that unnecessarily wastes her time. One night a week she manages to escape to her aerobics class, while the children's grandparents baby-sit.

Jenny: A 29 year old single mother

Example set of personas: Jack and Ellie

Jack – Child (Age 18 months)

Jack is now walking, but can't go far – and rarely in the direction you want him to! He frequently objects to being put in his buggy, as he finds it far more exciting to walk himself.

Around the house, objects have to be put out of his reach if they are fragile, potentially dangerous or could be used as a 'weapon' for attacking his sister Ellie.

Although Jack is at a delightful age, he is also quite time-consuming to look after as he's constantly absorbed with learning about his environment.

Ellie – Child (Age 4)

Ellie has just left part-time nursery and started her foundation year at the local school. She is rapidly becoming more independent. Ellie is obsessed with anything pink or related to Barbie or Girls Aloud and would happily dress as a ballerina or fairy every day if she could.

Ellie is learning to read and attempts to read everything she can around the house. She is at an impressionable age and wants very much to be part of the 'in-crowd' socially.

Jack: An 18 month old child

Ellie: A 4 year old child

Example set of personas: Carol

Grandmother (age 57)

Carol has a part-time job in a local arts and crafts shop. She is currently learning to use a computer to help out with enquiries that come through the shop's web site.

She is normally very active but has recently been hampered by a broken wrist sustained in a fall. Although she usually deals with problems in an optimistic and positive manner, she is finding the plaster cast very cumbersome. Many everyday tasks are now difficult and time-consuming.

Carol is particularly frustrated by not being able to help and play with her grandchildren as much, especially as Ellie desperately wants her grandmother to finish the fairy costume she's been making for her.

Carol: A 57 year old grandmother

Example set of personas: David

Grandad (age 60)

Recently retired, David spends most days pottering around the garden and playing golf. At weekends, he enjoys walking in the countryside with his wife, Carol. He is currently searching for a walking holiday for them on the Internet.

Although generally fit and healthy, David has become hard of hearing, but struggles to accept it. He does have a hearing aid and, like his reading glasses, it is another thing that Carol often has to search for.

David doesn't see himself as old, particularly as he helps care for his mother-in-law, Rose.

David: A 60 year old grandad

Example set of personas: Rose

Great-grandmother (age 83)

Rose lives 15 minutes drive away from David and Carol. Although fiercely independent, she struggles with everyday tasks like shopping, cooking and housework. Carol and David need to come round most days to help.

She still greatly enjoys an active social life - including her regular bridge and quiz night every week and going out for meals with the whole family.

Unlike David, Rose has come to accept her hearing aid as a necessity. She has worn reading glasses for many years and always carries them with her.

Rose: An 83 year old great-grandmother

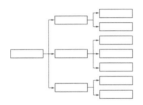

Task analysis

John Clarkson and Sam Waller

Task analysis is often used during conceptual design to help generate possible solutions. However, it may also be employed during the definition phase to assist in the elaboration of requirements, or when evaluating the capability requirements for an existing product.

Functional analysis provides a means for expressing the problem (without specifying a particular solution) and provides a graphical way to view these requirements. It encourages the designer to trace through each function of the product, making it more likely that all functional requirements will be captured.

Functional analysis is used to break down system-level goals into smaller components, each of which can then, if appropriate, be broken down further. There are many approaches to functional analysis, however, the Functional Analysis System Technique (FAST) has proved particularly useful for product design.

The FAST approach encourages users to define high level functions that need to be accomplished on the left hand side of the page, then progressively identify sub-functions by adding further boxes to the right of each high-level function. The following pages explore
- Tips for functional analysis
- Lifecycle analysis

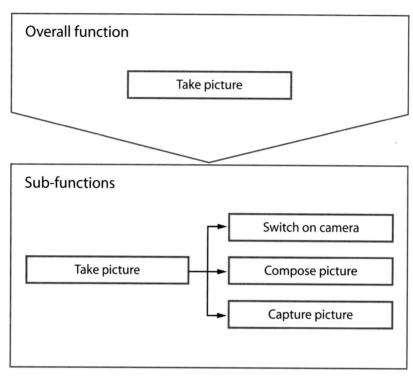

A functional analysis starts with a high level description of the
overall function, which is then broken down into sub-functions

Tips for functional analysis

The construction of the FAST diagram may be made easier by using the following tips

- Start by identifying general functions and then get more specific by asking 'how?' – name each function with a verb/noun pair

- Chronologically trace through each function that must be accomplished – this makes it less likely that any key requirements will be missed

- Include all special modes of operation such as stand-by, run, cleaning – functions that are not part of the normal operation are as important as those that are

- Avoid specifying form, structure or solutions – functions should describe behaviour, rather than embodiment

- Customise the FAST diagram – the more information that can be visualised, the more helpful it is

In addition, the operation of most products and services divides readily into 'ready-go-stop' functions.

- **Ready** – prepare, set, initialise

- **Go** – operate, start, steps of operation

- **Stop** – clean up, dispose, save data

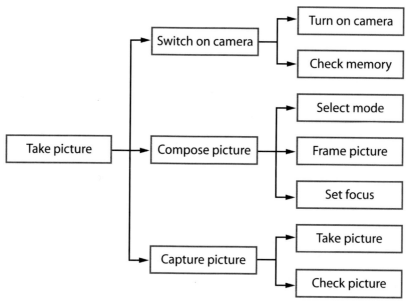

A further breakdown of sub-functions into lower-level functions

Lifecycle analysis

It is important to consider the whole lifecycle of the product, not just its main use. This might include manufacture, distribution, support and disposal.

In addition, there may be other functions relevant to the use of the product, from the point of purchase to the point of disposal.

When trying to articulate the detailed requirements for each function, it may be helpful to consider the following questions

- **How well?** e.g. quality

- **How often?** e.g. rate

- **How fast?** e.g. cycle time

- **How safe?** e.g. safety targets

- **How much?** e.g. costs

- **How soon?** e.g. schedule

- **How recorded?** e.g. documentation

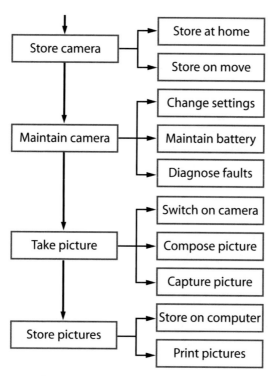

The functional analysis can be further expanded to consider tasks that occur throughout the whole lifecycle of the product

Evaluation tools

Joy Goodman and Sam Waller

Overview

The following tools can be used throughout the design process, in order to evaluate concepts or solutions to achieve more inclusive designs. Many of these tools are used in conjunction with task and lifecycle analysis.

 **Capability simulators**

 **Expert appraisal**

 **User involvement**

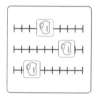 **Capability assessment**

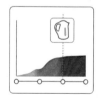 **Exclusion audit**

Capability simulators: Introduction

Capability simulators are devices that designers can use to reduce their ability to interact with a product.

- Physical simulators are devices that can be worn to impair movement or vision

- Software simulators modify an audio clip or photo image, so that a fully able person perceives the information as though he or she has a capability loss

These simulators can provide a quick and cheap method to help designers empathise with those who have capability losses, increase their understanding of the different losses, and simulate how exclusion occurs during product interaction. The cost, speed and ease of access means that these simulators can be used both early on and repeatedly throughout the design process.

However, no simulator can ever truly model what it is like to live with a particular capability reduction on an everyday basis. In addition, the decline in cognitive ability, and the effect of the user's past experience cannot be meaningfully reproduced by simulation. Simulators are helpful to increase empathy with users who have reduced capability, but should never be considered as a replacement for involving real people with such losses.

Physical and software simulators can be used
throughout the design process

Coping strategies are developed by users with capability losses, which
are unlikely to be accounted for when a designer uses a simulator

Capability simulators: Physical simulators

During physical simulation of capability loss, the person assessing the product wears items to 'reproduce' the effects of different types and levels of motor and sensory impairments.

Simple simulators can be created from everyday products that reduce freedom of movement in key parts of the body, such as gloves or sports braces. Spectacles smeared with grease can also be used to simulate decreases in vision capability. Alternatively, organisations such as Visual Impairment North East supply glasses representing different eye conditions.

Current research within Cambridge University is aiming to use special glasses that model vision impairment, together with devices that can be worn to limit finger motion and elbow extension. Future research will attempt to link the capability levels encountered while wearing the simulators, to the number of people with that capability level.

Simple vision simulators can be created using glasses and grease, while Cambridge University have developed a glove that simulates impairment

A phone viewed with no impairment simulated, and the same phone viewed through glasses that simulate vision impairment

Visual Impairment North East www.vine-simspecs.org.uk

Capability simulators: Software simulators

Research within Cambridge University has developed software that can simulate a variety of vision and hearing impairments, and these simulators are available on www.inclusivedesigntoolkit.com

The vision simulator modifies a digital image to show what the image might look like when viewed with a variety of different vision conditions. Each condition can be applied with different severity levels.

Different design concepts can quickly be compared to assess their appearance with visual impairments.

The hearing simulator modifies an audio file to simulate hearing conditions such as the natural deterioration caused with ageing. Different sounds can be compared to see how they are affected by this loss, and the effect of the ambient background noise can also be appreciated.

Other recommended simulators are detailed within the Useful resources section of Part 1: Introduction.

A toaster viewed with full vision capability, compared to the same toaster viewed with reduced contrast sensitivity

A suggested redesign improves contrast of areas so users with reduced contrast sensitivity can still identify the controls

Expert appraisal

Expert appraisal is the evaluation of a product or service by someone who has the professional training or experience to make an informed judgement on the design. Ideally, this person should not be biased by former involvement with the product since familiarity with any product or task makes it seem simpler and easier. Expert appraisal can be used to

- **Identify** possible causes of design exclusion

- **Suggest** improvements to reduce this exclusion

- **Increase** user satisfaction

Experts may include usability professionals, engineers, other designers, or experts with suitable knowledge of the product type or its particular environment. It is essential that the expert has a sound knowledge of the range of users that need to be considered and the circumstances of their interaction. Achieving reliable results through this method often requires the participation of several specialists, so that different perspectives and problems can be identified.

It is desirable to have an internal 'user champion' who can provide information about the user's perspective throughout the design process. Expert appraisal is usually used to detect critical problems and to provide priorities for exploration with users. However, it can also provide valuable improvement suggestions throughout the design process.

Expert appraisal is the evaluation of a product or service by someone who has professional training or relevant experience

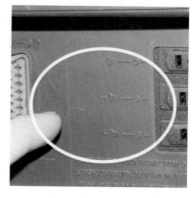

The small size, poor contrast, and lack of explanatory text means that many users will not be able to see or understand these symbols

User involvement: Introduction

Involving real end-users at any or all stages of the design process can provide insight into what design solutions can and cannot be used, and what goals they want to achieve with the product.

The focus of this toolkit is inclusive design and how this varies from traditional approaches. Involving real people is essential to understand the needs and goals that the product will address. User needs and goals extend beyond the boundaries of product interaction; however, this toolkit focuses on interaction since it is often misunderstood and its importance underestimated.

Users are those who will (attempt to) use the product or service once it is on the market. In practice, the type(s) of person that the product is aimed at will need to be determined, so people who represent these real end-users can be selected to engage in the design process.

Potential users vary widely, so it is of critical importance to select an appropriate mix of people for any study. As previously discussed, it is also important to ensure that the least able and most vulnerable users are considered. Members of the design team are therefore often not representative users.

Involving real end-users at any or all stages of the design process can
provide insight into what design solutions can and cannot be used

User Involvement: Participants

Different stages in the design process require different kinds of information, so the most appropriate users to involve and how to involve them may vary from stage to stage.

Involving large numbers of users improves accuracy but can be expensive. Useful feedback can be obtained from smaller numbers of users. In practice, within a single category of users

- The majority of problems can be identified with 10 users

- At least 3 users of any one type are needed to reduce biases from user responses and observations

Various organisations can provide access to users

- Ricability www.ricability.org.uk

- User associations, such as the Royal National Institute for the Blind, Royal National Institute for the Deaf, and Help the Aged

Who to involve?		Aim
Broad user mix	– Users from a range of market segments	To understand general user requirements
Boundary users	– Users on the limit of being able to use the product	To identify opportunities for design improvement
Extreme users	– Users with a severe loss of capability	To inspire creativity during concept development
Mixed experience users	– Users with different levels of experience with similar products	To understand the impact of experience on use
Community groups	– Groups of users who share experience of interacting with similar products	To provide a broad understanding of product use

The types and aims of user involvement

Evaluation tools

User involvement: Techniques

There are many different ways of involving users in the design process, and these can be categorised into three main types: ask, observe or participate.

Ask the users directly about their lives, what they want or need or what they think of the design. However, be aware that people often struggle to clearly articulate their real needs due to

- Lack of acceptance of their own deficiencies

- Inability to imagine what could be

- Poor awareness of their own habits and practices

- Filtering opinions to what they think you want to hear

Multiple techniques may need to be used to get to the heart of a user's real needs.

Observe what users do. Watch them in daily life to understand their experiences and needs, or use methods such as video-ethnography. Consider the use of a controlled observation, where it is possible to watch and video users carrying out specified tasks with a product prototype.

Alternatively, participative methods consider users as co-designers, providing direct input into the creative process.

For more information on user involvement, see Aldersley-Williams (1999) and IDEO (2003).

Asking users direct questions complements insight gained
from observing them using products in their daily lives

Involving users as co-designers can produce
innovative and effective designs

Aldersey-Williams H et al (1999) The Methods Lab: User Research for Design, Design for Ageing Network. www.education.edean.org/pdf/Tool039.pdf
IDEO (2003) Method Cards. Palo Alto, IDEO

Capability assessment

A capability assessment provides a quick and simple way to evaluate products or concepts by comparing the capability levels required to use them. The use of any product can be broken down into a series of activities, where each activity forms part of a wider product interaction via a task or lifecycle analysis.

For each activity, demands are made on the user. These demands can be rated according to a series of capability scales. At their simplest, these scales range from low to high, where low and high provide a relative measure when one product or scale is compared to another.

Although these scale measurements are crude, they are easy to use as an initial tool and can provide an effective visual comparison between alternative products or concepts. Reducing capability demands (while achieving the same features or functions) should lead to a more satisfying product that can be used by a wider percentage of the population.

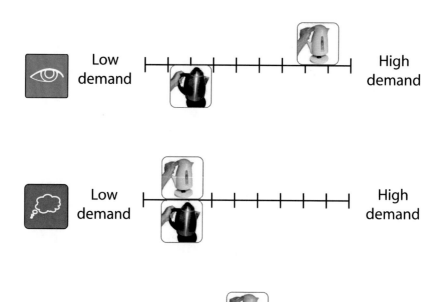

Products can be assessed for capability demands in different
categories, such as vision, thinking and dexterity

Exclusion audit: The basics

An exclusion audit is a tool to evaluate different products or concepts by comparing the proportion of the population that will be unable to use them. This allows design decisions to be based on meaningful numbers, but requires greater levels of knowledge, resources and time than a capability assessment. A task analysis is used to record the activities that are necessary to use the product, then the capability demands of these activities are assessed in terms of the levels of exclusion that result.

Objective scales may be used to measure the level of capability that a product or service demands in order to use it. Once the appropriate demand level has been identified, the data from the 1996/97 Disability Follow-up Survey (Grundy 1999) can provide the number of people that will be excluded. The statements used to describe the anchor points, and the graphs for each different capability type can be found within Part 4: User capabilities.

Since any product interaction usually requires a particular sequence of tasks, and each task may require the use of multiple capabilities, a more complex calculation is often required. In this case, an exclusion calculator (available from www.inclusivedesigntoolkit.com) can be used.

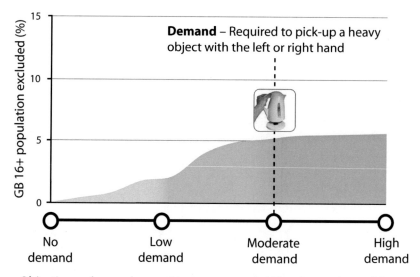

Objective scales can be used to measure capability demands, enabling the use of prevalence data to estimate the number of people excluded

Grundy E, Ahlburg D, Ali M, Breeze E, Sloggett A (1999) Research report 94 - Disability in Great Britain. Corporate Document Services, London, UK. ISBN 1-84123-119-3.

Evaluation tools

Exclusion audit: Further details

The population data from an exclusion audit can be used to select design improvements that will benefit the greatest number of people. For example, given a particular product, a slight reduction in vision demand could make a significant difference to the number of people excluded, whereas a major reduction in dexterity demand might be required to achieve any real benefit.

The number of people excluded becomes more meaningful when an exclusion audit is combined with a task analysis, which explains how several different activities combine together to form a higher-level function. For example, the initial set-up of a video recorder includes activities such as opening the packaging, and plugging in cables.

In this case, the advantage in reducing the dexterity required to plug in the cables could be minimal if opening the packaging needs a higher dexterity requirement anyway. It is also important to consider where exclusion occurs throughout the whole lifecycle of the product.

Exclusion audits can be highly beneficial but may require an expert in the field to achieve numbers that are correct and meaningful. To obtain further information, see the front of this book for contact details of the authoring institutions.

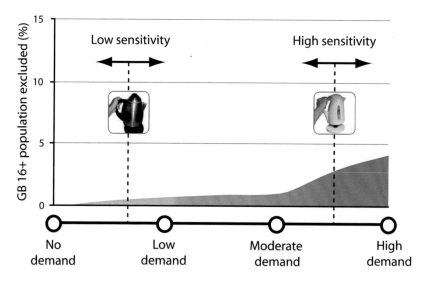

Minor variations in demand may significantly affect exclusion, depending upon the shape of the graph at the current demand level

User capabilities

Part 4: User capabilities

Carlos Cardoso, John Clarkson, Pat Langdon
Umesh Persad and Sam Waller

User capabilities

The framework section describes a model of interaction between the different user capabilities, and also shows how the population data and design guidance for each capability should be interpreted. The user capabilities are grouped into three categories, which are **sensory** (vision and hearing), **cognitive** (thinking and communication) and **motor** (locomotion, reach & stretch and dexterity).

Contents

User capabilities

Framework

Sam Waller and John Clarkson

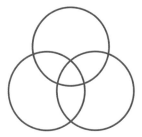

Overview

This section introduces a framework for relating data regarding user capabilities to descriptions of products and their interfaces. It acts as an introduction to seven further sections describing capabilities particularly relevant to product interaction.

When reviewing the capability demands associated with using a particular product it is important to consider all seven categories since many people, especially those in older age groups, experience more than one capability loss in the form of multiple minor impairments.

Framework

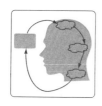 **A model of product interaction**

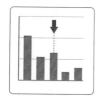 **Assessing capability levels**

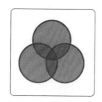 **The disability survey**

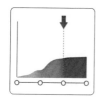 **Assessing demand and exclusion**

 **Using design guidance**

 **Design example**

Framework

A model of product interaction

Any interaction with a product or service typically requires a cycle where the user

- Perceives

- Thinks

- Acts

Perceiving and acting both require sensory and motor capabilities. In addition, the body's sensory and motor resources are controlled by the brain and therefore require cognitive capability.

For example, perceiving text on a product can rely on the hands to move and orientate the product for visual examination or the eyes could guide the fingers to press particular buttons. However, for the most part, perceiving requires sensory capability, thinking requires cognitive capability, and acting requires motor capability.

The interaction between a product and the user's capabilities is also influenced by the environment in which the product is used. For example, low, or indeed high, ambient light levels can compromise a user's ability to read.

Framework

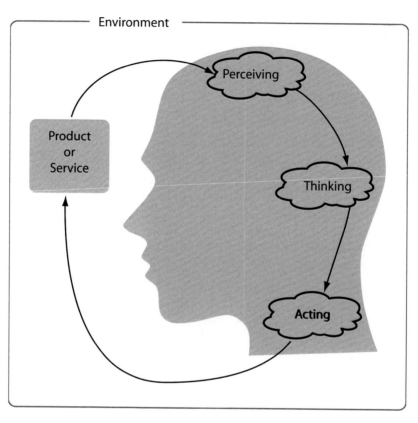

An interaction with a product involves a cycle where the user's
capabilities are used to perceive, think and then act

Assessing capability levels

The following seven capability categories are helpful to measure a person's capability, or assess the ability level that a product demands in order to use it.

- **Vision** is the ability to use the colour and brightness of light to detect objects, discriminate between different surfaces, or the detail on a surface

- **Hearing** is the ability to discriminate specific tones or speech from ambient noise and to tell where the sounds are coming from

- **Thinking** is the ability to process information, hold attention, store and retrieve memories, and also select appropriate responses and actions

- **Communication** is the ability to understand other people, and express oneself to others (this inevitably overlaps with vision, hearing, and thinking)

- **Locomotion** is the ability to move around, bend down, climb steps, and shift the body between standing, sitting and kneeling

- **Reach & stretch** is the ability to put one or both arms out in front of the body, above the head, or behind the back

- **Dexterity** is the ability of one or both hands to perform fine finger manipulation, pick up and carry objects, or grasp and squeeze objects

Sensory capability includes vision and hearing. Cognitive capability includes thinking and communication. Motor capability includes locomotion, reach & stretch and dexterity.

Framework

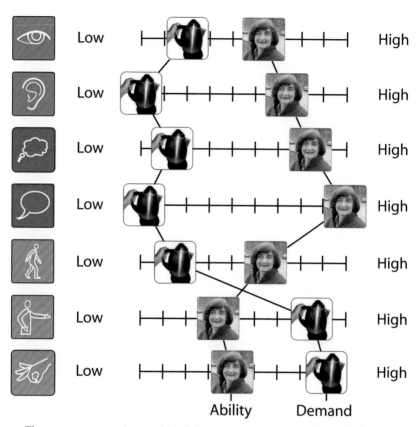

Ability   Demand

The seven categories are helpful to measure a person's capability, or assess the ability level that a product demands in order to use it

The disability survey: Introduction

The 1996/97 Family Resources Survey was commissioned by the UK government to provide statistics about households in Great Britain. In the same years, the Disability Follow-up to the Family Resources Survey was performed in order to help plan welfare support for disabled people.

People were selected for the Disability Follow-up Survey if they met certain criteria, such as being in receipt of incapacity benefit. Approximately 7500 participants were asked up to 300 questions regarding whether they were able to perform certain tasks such as

" Can you see well enough to read a newspaper headline? "

The results were collated to provide estimates for the national prevalence of disability (Grundy 1999). This survey is the most recent to consider all seven capability categories, and is therefore the only source suitable for considering multiple capability losses. According to the definition used in the survey, 17.8 % of the GB adult population have less than full ability in one or more categories. The GB adult population was 45.6 million people at the time of the survey.

The following pages explore further details of the disability survey, followed by the prevalence data and definitions of full ability for Sensory capabilities, Cognitive capabilities, and Motor capabilities.

Framework

4-10

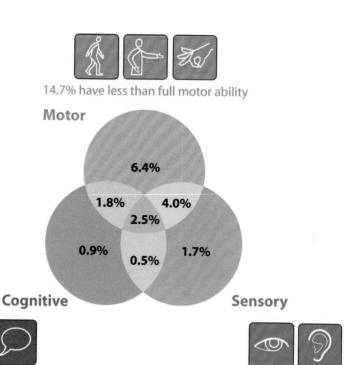

14.7% have less than full motor ability

Motor

6.4%

1.8% 4.0%

2.5%

0.9% 1.7%

0.5%

Cognitive

Sensory

5.7% have less than full cognitive ability

8.7% have less than full sensory ability

Prevalence of capability loss, where the overlapping circles indicate the population that has capability losses in multiple categories

Grundy E, Ahlburg D, Ali M, Breeze E, Sloggett A (1999) Research report 94 - Disability in Great Britain. Corporate Document Services, London, UK. ISBN 1-84123-119-3.

Framework

The disability survey: Further details

The questions within the Disability Follow-up Survey can be used to estimate the number of people that would be unable to perform a certain task that is required to use a product, and would therefore be excluded.

The 300 survey questions were combined to form ability levels that could measure quality of life impairment, often using multiple questions to create each level. However, the manner in which the questions were combined can make the levels difficult to interpret for product interaction.

Further research will create more useful ability levels from the original survey questions, and specifically collect additional capability data for the purpose of calculating exclusion. Until then, the Disability Follow-up Survey remains the best source of coherent data for estimating design exclusion.

Framework

Survey questions

" Can you turn a tap or control knob
     ... with your right hand?
     ... with your left hand? "

" Can you pick up a small object like a safety pin
     ... with your right hand?
     ... with your left hand? "

" Can you tie a bow in laces or string without difficulty? "

Dexterity ability levels

D10   Can turn a tap or control know with one hand but not the other. Can squeeze water from a sponge with one hand but not the other

D11   Can pick up a small object such as a safety pin with one hand but not the other. Can pick up and carry a pint of milk with one hand but not the other. Has difficulty tying a bow in laces or strings

The 300 questions from the Disability Follow-up Survey were combined to form ability levels that could measure quality of life impairment

Framework

The disability survey: Sensory capability

Sensory capability describes the combination of vision and hearing capabilities. The Disability Follow-up Survey found that 8.7% of the GB adult population have less than full ability in one or both of these categories. The GB adult population was 45.6 million people at the time of the survey.

A person with full **vision** ability can see well enough to

- Recognise a friend across the road without difficulty

- Read ordinary newsprint without difficulty

A person with full **hearing** ability can hear well enough to

- Follow a conversation during background noise without great difficulty

- Follow a TV programme at a volume that others find acceptable

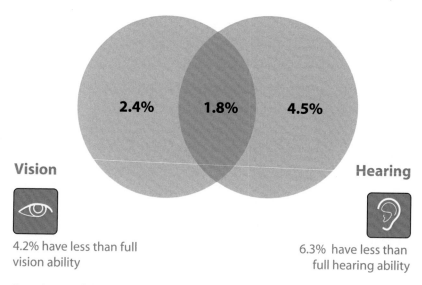

Vision

4.2% have less than full
vision ability

Hearing

6.3% have less than
full hearing ability

Prevalence of the population with less than full ability in vision and
hearing, where the overlapping circles indicate the population that has
capability losses in both categories

The disability survey: Cognitive capability

Cognitive capability describes the combination of thinking and communication capabilities. The Disability Follow-up Survey found that 5.7% of the GB adult population have less than full ability in one or both of these categories. The GB adult population was 45.6 million people at the time of the survey.

A person with full **thinking** ability can perform tasks such as

- Hold a conversation, without losing track of what is being said

- Write a short letter to someone without help

- Count well enough to handle money

- Remember a message and pass it on

- Remember the names of friends and family that are seen regularly

A person with full **communication** ability can

- Communicate with strangers with no difficulty

Each person's thinking ability was measured by counting up the number of everyday tasks they were unable to perform. This approach does not relate to cognitive science which makes it particularly challenging to interpret the results in terms of product exclusion.

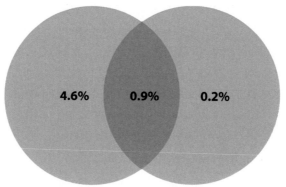

Thinking

5.5% have less than full
thinking ability

Communication

1.1% have less than full
communication ability

Prevalence of the population with less than full ability in thinking and
communication, where the overlapping circles indicate the population
that has capability losses in both categories

Framework

The disability survey: Motor capability

Motor capability describes the combination of locomotion, reach & stretch, and dexterity capabilities. The Disability Follow-up Survey found that 14.7% of the GB adult population have less than full ability in one or more of these categories. The GB adult population was 45.6 million people at the time of the survey.

A person with full **locomotion** ability can
- Walk 350 metres ($\approx$ 400 yds) without stopping
- Ascend/descend a flight of 12 steps without handrails and without resting
- Bend down to use a dustpan and brush and then straighten up again

A person with full **reach & stretch** ability can
- Raise both arms out in front, up to the head, or behind the back

A person with full **dexterity** ability can
- Tie a bow in laces with no difficulty
- Pick up and carry a 2.5 kg bag of potatoes in each hand
- Squeeze a sponge with each hand

The Disability Follow-Up Survey only measured reach & stretch relative to the person's own body, so it is not possible to convert this to standard measurements like 'can reach to 2.0 metres.'

6.6% have less than full dexterity ability

Dexterity

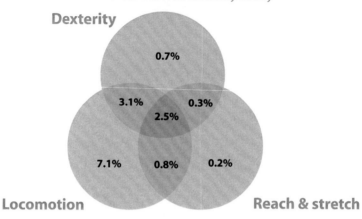

0.7%

3.1%   0.3%

2.5%

7.1%   0.8%   0.2%

Locomotion   **Reach & stretch**

13.5% have less than
full locomotion ability

3.8% have less than full
reach & stretch ability

Prevalence of the population with less than full ability in locomotion,
reach & stretch, and dexterity, where the overlapping circles indicate the
population that has capability losses in one or more categories

Demand and exclusion: The basics

The results from the Disability Follow-up Survey were presented in terms of the number of people with specific levels of disability. For vision, level V1 refers to extreme disability, V9 is mild disability, and V10 is full vision ability.

For the purpose of inclusive design, it is more useful to consider V1, V2 and V3 as being increasing levels of vision ability. For example, those in ability level V3 **can** tell by the light where the windows are (opposite of V1), and they **can** see the shapes of furniture in a room (opposite of V2), but they **cannot** recognize a friend if close to his face.

In order to estimate design exclusion, it is necessary to sum together the ability bands, to work out the total number of people who would be unable to perform a specific task.

For example, supposing a product required the user to see well enough to read a newspaper headline. The number of people excluded would be the sum of people in categories V1-V5, which is approximately 1% of the GB adult population.

However, if the required task is not specifically mentioned on the scale, then some judgment will be required to position the task between existing ability levels. The next page shows the same data presented in a suitable format to achieve this.

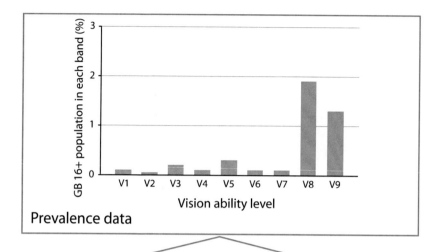

Prevalence data

V1 Cannot tell by the light where the windows are

V2 Cannot see the shapes of furniture in a room

V3 Cannot see well enough to recognise a friend if close to his face

V4 Cannot see well enough to recognise a friend at arm's length away

V5 Cannot see well enough to read a newspaper headline

Vision ability levels

Definitions of some of the ability levels from the Disability Follow-up Survey and the corresponding number of people within each level

Demand and exclusion: Further details

The data from the Disability Follow-Up Survey can also be presented in a format suitable for assessing design exclusion directly, where the ability level that a product demands in order to use it is directly plotted against the number of people who will be excluded.

For example, with regard to vision demand, approximately 1% of the GB adult population would be excluded from a product that requires the user to see well enough to read a newspaper headline.

The Disability Follow-Up Survey does not make any reference to the environment, or to fatigue caused by repeated actions. Until better data is obtained, these factors can only be accounted for by using judgement to modify the demand level appropriately

Estimating the number of people who would be unable to use a product based on multiple different capability demands requires an exclusion calculator, which is available from www.inclusivedesigntoolkit.com

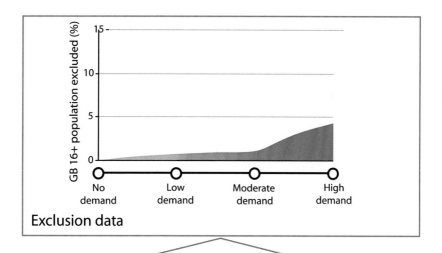

Exclusion data

No demand

The user is not required to perceive anything by sight

Low demand

The user is required to have sufficient ability to do things like read a newspaper headline, or recognise a friend at arm's length away

Vision demand levels

The data from the Disability Follow-up Survey is presented in a format suitable for assessing design exclusion

Using design guidance

Within each capability section, guidance is provided to help design products and services that are more usable by people who are impaired in that capability.

The guidance provides suggestions and highlights issues that need to be considered, but is not a set of rules to be strictly followed, nor a list of items that can be 'checked' to guarantee a successful and inclusive design. The advice works effectively within the context of an Inclusive design process as elaborated in Part 2.

Successful application of the design guidance requires understanding the needs and characteristics of the target users, developed through a discovery phase at the start of the design process.

The design guidance should also be supplemented by consultation with experts in the relevant capabilities and with users who have capability losses (elaborated further within Part 3: Knowledge and tools). Such consultation enables the guidance to be better interpreted, and can evaluate whether capability range of the target users matches appropriately with the demands made by the product or service.

For more information on using design guidance, see Nicolle and Abascal (2001).

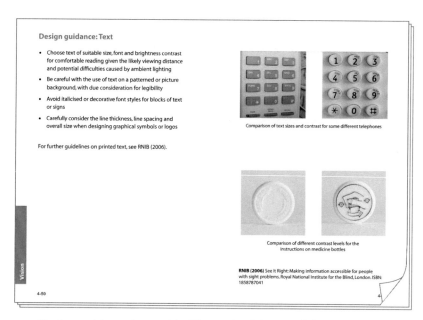

Design guidance: Text

- Choose text of suitable size, font and brightness contrast for comfortable reading given the likely viewing distance and potential difficulties caused by ambient lighting
- Be careful with the use of text on a patterned or picture background, with due consideration for legibility
- Avoid italicised or decorative font styles for blocks of text or signs
- Carefully consider the line thickness, line spacing and overall size when designing graphical symbols or logos

For further guidelines on printed text, see RNIB (2006).

Comparison of text sizes and contrast for some different telephones

Comparison of different contrast levels for the instructions on medicine bottles

RNIB (2006) See it Right: Making information accessible for people with sight problems. Royal National Institute for the Blind, London. ISBN: 1858787041

Vision

4-50

Design guidance is provided for each of the capability categories

Framework

Nicolle C and Abascal J (2001) Inclusive design guidelines for HCI. Taylor and Francis, London UK.

Design example

The principles of demand and exclusion can be used to estimate the number of people who would be unable to use the kettle shown opposite. For the sake of simplicity, the results only consider vision and dexterity.

The tasks required to use the kettle are identified as: separate kettle from power source, carry to water source, fill the kettle to desired level, re-attach to power source, switch on, and finally, pour the boiling water into mug. The level of design exclusion for an ideal kettle would be no greater than the number of people who would be unable to pick up and drink hot liquid from a mug, which is also analysed for comparison.

The revised capability scales were used to assess the demand level for the tasks required to use each product, then the exclusion calculator from www.inclusivedesigntoolkit.com was used to estimate the proportion of the population that would be unable to perform these tasks.

The combined number of people excluded from using the kettle (7.0%) is less than the total for each separate capability (6.5 + 0.9 = 7.4%), because some people have both low dexterity and vision capability, but are counted only once in the combined exclusion estimate.

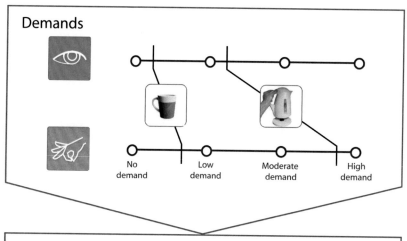

Demands

No demand   Low demand   Moderate demand   High demand

Exclusion levels

	Mug	Kettle
Dexterity	0.5%	6.5%
Vision	0.4%	0.9%
Combined	0.9%	7.0%

Assessment of demand levels associated with using a mug and a kettle, and calculation of the corresponding proportion of the GB adult population that would be excluded

Framework

Vision

Umesh Persad and Pat Langdon

Overview

Our sense of vision allows us to perceive the world in images, motion and colour. We use information from the visual sense in order to move around and interact with objects and environments. The effective design of any product or environment should take into account the range of human visual abilities.

 **Understanding vision**

 **Visual functions**

 **Environmental context**

 **Design guidance**

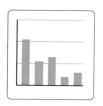 **Population statistics**

Vision

Understanding vision

The human eyes work by allowing light to enter through the pupil. The lens is used to focus light rays onto the retina, which is the surface at the back of the eye that is sensitive to light.

The retina consists of two types of receptor cells known as rods and cones. Rods allow us to differentiate between shades of black and white while cones allow us to see colour. Most cones are concentrated in a particularly sensitive region of the retina called the fovea. This region enables us to see the greatest detail. The receptor cells use the optic nerve to transmit signals to the brain, which interprets the signals from both eyes to construct the image we see. The combined image from both eyes assists depth perception.

Common conditions such as short and long-sightedness can occur due to a misshapen lens or eyeball, and can be corrected by glasses. However, as the eye muscles weaken, or the lens becomes stiffer, the eye can no longer adapt to focus on objects at different distances.

Because of ageing and various eye conditions, the structure and function of the eye can also deteriorate, which can result in blurry vision, central or peripheral loss of visual field, and reduced contrast sensitivity. Colour blindness is mainly inherited as a genetic defect, although the ability to distinguish between blue and green can decrease with age.

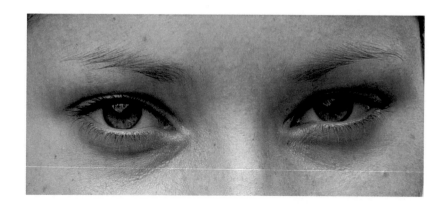

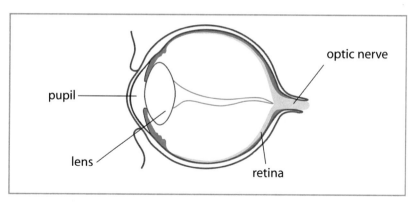

The shape and structure of eyes

Visual functions: Introduction

The visual system serves various functions, four of which are discussed in the context of designing products.

- Visual acuity is the ability to see fine details of objects

- Contrast sensitivity is the ability to discriminate between different brightness levels

- Colour perception is the ability to distinguish between different colours

- Usable visual field is the ability to use the whole of the visual field to perceive detail in the area being looked at and the surrounding area

A mobile phone viewed with no impairment, compared to the same phone viewed with reduced visual acuity

Mobile phone seen with reduced contrast sensitivity and red-green colour blindness

Visual functions: Visual acuity

Visual acuity is the ability of the eye to see fine detail. Being able to see details depends on several factors

- The ability of the lens to focus the light given the viewing distance

- The smallest feature or space that the retina can resolve (for example, text size or stroke thickness)

- The clarity of the fluid and membranes that the light passes through to reach the retina

- The ambient illumination and the contrast between the foreground and background

Reading text is the most common task with a high acuity demand. The matrix opposite shows various combinations of text size and font style. Consider the following when choosing text style

- The ease with which characters within a font can be recognised depends on the thickness and spacing of the lines that make up the character, together with the uniqueness of the character's shape

- Legibility and reading comfort are both reduced for underlined, italicised or decorative font styles

- Ensuring that characters remain unique after being reflected or rotated can help those with dyslexia

Visual tasks requiring acuity also include identifying graphics and symbols, reading signage and recognising faces.

Vision

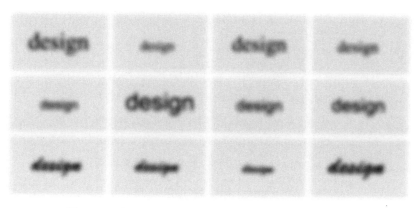

design design design design

design **design** design **design**

design *design* *design* *design*

Different combinations of font size and style – the top line is a serif font,
the middle line a sans serif font, and bottom line a decorative font

The same images viewed with reduced visual acuity

Visual functions: Contrast sensitivity

Colour can be described by its hue, saturation and brightness (how much light is apparently reflected). Contrast sensitivity is the ability to perceive the difference in brightness between a foreground colour and a background colour. It is related to the size, distance and illumination of the object to be detected. Maximum contrast occurs with white on black or vice versa.

Higher contrast levels result in a greater likelihood of detection by people with low contrast sensitivity. For example, the ability to distinguish number keys from the body of a mobile phone depends on their contrast, the viewing distance, the size of the text and the ambient illumination.

Visual acuity is related to contrast, and low contrast text will be more difficult to discriminate than high contrast text. In addition, controls on products need to be of sufficient contrast against product chassis to be easily detected. Contrast sensitivity is important for activities such as detecting and reading text, moving around in the environment, and detecting the outlines of buildings, roads, and pavements.

The diagrams opposite show some different foreground and background colours for text and the corresponding images viewed with a reduced brightness contrast. Note how a sharp colour distinction helps to discriminate between the foreground and background when the brightness contrast is reduced.

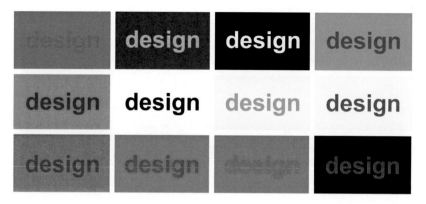

To determine which colour combinations are effective, try viewing this image at various distances from your eyes and squinting as you read it

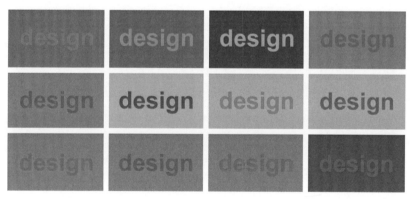

The same images viewed with reduced brightness contrast

Visual functions: Colour perception

Colour conveys information about the physical world. Loss of colour discrimination (or colour blindness) is the inability to distinguish between various colours. The notion that people with colour blindness cannot perceive colour is inaccurate, and in fact total loss of colour perception is extremely rare. A person who is colour blind cannot effectively distinguish between different colours in the colour spectrum.

The most common form of colour blindness is red-green colour blindness, where the ability to distinguish between colours from red to green in the colour spectrum is reduced. These colour confusions can make interaction with products difficult if colour alone is used to provide information.

The diagram opposite shows various foreground and background colour combinations (top) and the corresponding simulated appearance for a red-green colour blind person (bottom). Note that images that have similar brightness contrasts can disappear when viewed by someone with colour blindness.

Vision

To determine which colour combinations are effective, try viewing this image at various distances from your eyes and squinting as you read it

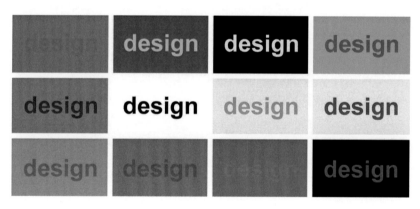

The same images viewed with a simulated red-green colour blindness

Visual functions: Usable visual field

With increasing age and various eye conditions, the usable field of view can change. This loss can either start from the centre of the visual field (central field loss) or from the outer edge of visual field (peripheral field loss).

The central visual field is used for focusing and perceiving detail. When the central field is obscured, tasks that require perception of detail (such as reading) become very difficult. People generally adapt to compensate for this loss and attempt to use the peripheral visual field. However, this part of the retina is less sensitive, resulting in a loss of acuity and contrast sensitivity. The same guidance given for acuity and contrast will help users with central field loss.

A reduction in the usable peripheral visual field results in tunnel vision and can affect mobility. A rail ticket machine with widely spaced controls can result in problems when viewed with a peripheral loss. The lower figures indicate a proposed redesign of the same machine where the continuity between the required action areas has been emphasised, resulting in a more usable interface.

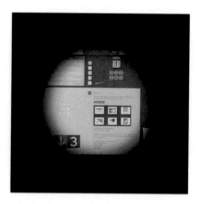

A ticket machine that has poor clarity of layout, and the same
ticket machine viewed with poor peripheral vision

A redesigned layout for the same machine, which enables the
overall layout to be perceived, even with a peripheral vision loss.

Environmental context

The 'apparent' size of an object is directly proportional to the distance it is away. Successfully visual perception depends primarily upon the brightness contrast, colour contrast and 'apparent' size of the detail to be perceived, the ability of the eye to successfully focus given the viewing distance and the ambient illumination. The environmental factors are now considered in further detail.

The level of ambient illumination, together with the spatial relations between the light source, the product, and the user, impact on the ability to perceive visual detail. Examples highlighting this include reading the text on the back of a television, or reading a road sign whilst facing the sun.

Glare can cause significant difficulties when reflective surfaces such as a screen are viewed from a certain angle related to the sun or light source. Consideration of reflectivity, distance and viewing angle is particularly significant when the position of the product or user is fixed or constrained, such as when viewing a road-sign.

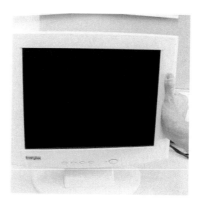

Tilt adjustment for a screen helps to minimise problems
with viewing angle and glare for a range of users

Viewing the back of equipment highlights difficulties
that can arise as a result of the context of use

Design guidance: General

- Consider potential issues with glare, based on
  - The surface finish of the item being looked at
  - The intensity of the light source
  - The spatial position of the surface, the viewer, and the light source with respect to the angle of view

- Contemplate enabling users to control the intensity, position, and angle of the lighting sources to best suit their own vision ability and the task

- Think about using colours to help convey information but ensure they are supplemented by presenting the information in alternative ways (e.g. use shapes and text)

- Consider using colour contrast to help make things stand out, but ensure there is also sufficient brightness contrast

- Check that a product remains usable when its image is converted to grey scale

- Think about assisting those with vision impairments by supplementing information through auditory or tactile means, with due consideration for information overload

- Arrange the design so that it remains visible and usable for those who have some loss of visual field

- Think about minimising exclusion by ensuring the design remains usable while wearing a vision impairment simulator

Vision

Comparison of mobile phones viewed with colour blindness –note how shape can be used so that the 'start call' and 'end call' buttons remain distinguishable

Shiny paper can cause glare problems, but matte paper finishes reduce problems with glare

Design guidance: Text

- Choose text of suitable size, font and brightness contrast for comfortable reading given the likely viewing distance and potential difficulties caused by ambient lighting

- Be careful with the use of text on a patterned or picture background, with due consideration for legibility

- Avoid italicised or decorative font styles for blocks of text or signs

- Carefully consider the line thickness, line spacing and overall size when designing graphical symbols or logos

- Note that common practice is to use a serif font for large blocks of text, and a sans serif font for signs, labels or headings

For further guidelines on printed text, see RNIB (2006).

Comparison of text sizes and contrast for some different telephones

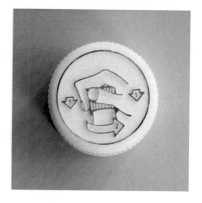

Comparison of different contrast levels for the
instructions on medicine bottles

RNIB (2006) See it Right: Making information accessible for people with
sight problems. Royal National Institute for the Blind, London.
ISBN: 1-85878-704-1

Vision

Population statistics: Prevalence data

Vision ability level (in increasing order)

V1   Cannot tell by the light where the windows are

V2   Cannot see the shapes of furniture in a room

V3   Cannot see well enough to recognise a friend if close to his face

V4   Cannot see well enough to recognise a friend who is at arm's length away

V5   Cannot see well enough to read a newspaper headline

V6   Cannot see well enough to read a large print book

V7   Cannot see well enough to recognise a friend across a room

V8   Has difficulty recognising a friend across the road

V9   Has difficulty reading ordinary newspaper print

V10 Full vision ability

Ability level is measured with any desired vision aids.

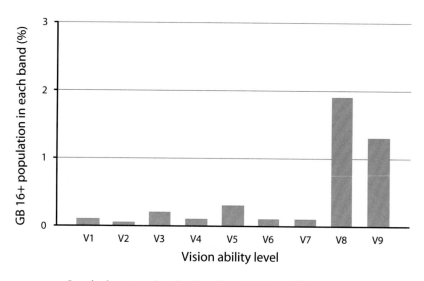

Graph showing the distribution of vision ability, where those with full ability (V10) are not shown

Important note

These ability levels and prevalence statistics are taken directly from the 1996/97 Disability Follow-up Survey (Grundy 1999), which was commissioned by the government to plan welfare support. The GB adult population was 45.6 million people at the time of the survey. Please see the Framework section within Part 4: User capabilities for more detail.

Grundy E, Ahlburg D, Ali M, Breeze E, Sloggett A (1999) Research report 94 - Disability in Great Britain. Corporate Document Services, London, UK. ISBN 1-84123-119-3.

Vision

Population statistics: Demand & exclusion

No demand

- The user is not required to perceive anything by sight

Low demand

The user is required to have sufficient ability to do things like

- Read a newspaper headline (≈ 72 pt text)

- Recognise a friend at arm's length away

Moderate demand

The user is required to have sufficient ability to do things like

- Read a large print book (≈ 16 pt text)

- Recognise a friend across the room

High demand

The user is required to have sufficient ability to do things like

- Read ordinary newsprint (≈ 9 pt text) without difficulty

- Recognise a friend across the road without difficulty

Demand levels assume that any desired vision aids will be used.

Vision

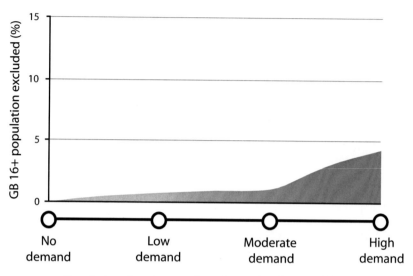

Graph showing the number of people who would be
excluded due to various levels of vision demand

Important note

These statements refer to the level of vision ability
that a product or service demands, in order to use it.
For a particular demand level, the 1996/97 Disability
Follow-up Survey is used to calculate the total number
of people who do not have this level of ability, and will
therefore be excluded. The GB adult population was
45.6 million people at the time of the survey. Please see
the Framework section within Part 4: User capabilities for
more detail.

Vision

Hearing

Umesh Persad and Pat Langdon

Overview

Hearing is the ability to interpret sound vibrations. People can identify simple sounds such as beeps and tones and complex sounds such as speech and music against differing background noise. Hearing also allows for speech perception which forms the basis of our ability to communicate with other.

 **Understanding hearing**

 **Hearing functions**

 **Environmental context**

 **Design guidance**

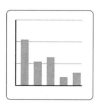 **Population statistics**

Understanding hearing

The human ear is divided into three parts: the outer ear, the middle ear and the inner ear. The outer ear collects sound energy and channels it to the middle ear via the ear drum. The sound energy is converted into mechanical vibrations of small bones in the middle ear. These vibrations are transmitted to cochlea in the inner ear.

A membrane in the cochlea picks up these vibrations and converts them into neural impulses. These impulses are then transmitted to the brain along the auditory nerve.

When blockages exist anywhere in the passage from the outer ear to the middle ear, they result in conductive hearing loss. This results in the loss of ability to hear faint sounds, and particularly those of high frequencies.

When the cochlea is affected by ageing or disease, it results in sensory neural hearing loss. This affects the quality of the sound detected and results in loss of ability to understand speech and discriminate various sounds, especially in the presence of noise. The ability to locate sounds also decreases with age, particularly for sounds with relatively low volume and short duration, such as the tones generated by watches.

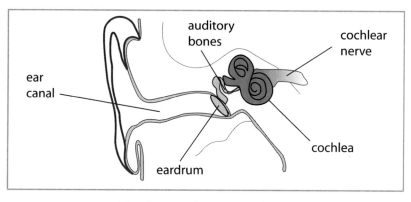

The shape and structure of ears

Hearing functions: Introduction

Three major hearing functions are considered in design applications.

- Sound detection is the ability to detect beeps, tones and other sound output from various products

- Speech discrimination is the ability to detect and understand speech in quiet and noisy environments

- Sound localisation is the ability to tell which direction a sound is coming from

Sound detection ability is needed to realise that a phone is ringing, while localisation ability helps to locate the phone, and speech discrimination is necessary to understand what the caller is saying

Hearing functions: Sound detection

Sound vibration can range from very low intensity to high intensity. This is perceived as loudness or volume. The frequency of these vibrations can also vary from low to high, and this is perceived as pitch.

Complex sounds such as speech and music contain a range of frequencies at various levels of intensity. In order to detect a sound, it must be of sufficient loudness and within a frequency range that is audible to the listener.

Detecting sounds in the presence of noise is more difficult than detecting sounds in isolation. For example, hearing a phone conversation in a crowded restaurant or hearing a phone ring while the television is on require the ability to distinguish sounds from background noise. Most real world tasks take place with some level of ambient noise.

Design inclusion can be maximised by allowing the user to customise the type and volume of the sounds emitted

Hearing functions: Speech discrimination

Human ability to discriminate speech is an important consideration when designing products that facilitate verbal communication or use speech output.

Examples include telephones, cash machines, car navigation systems, and accessible technology that aids people with low vision through alternative speech output.

Speech sounds can be detected when they are of sufficient loudness, but discrimination of speech can be difficult for some people, especially in the presence of noise.

Male or female voices can be used for speech. Generally male voices are of lower pitch and are within the range of hearing. Various accents and intonation can also affect how well speech is understood.

Speech output can be prerecorded and replayed or speech can be synthesised. Synthesised speech is more difficult for older people to understand.

Speech can become difficult to understand if it is recorded, played back or synthesised at high speed.

Following a conversation is more difficult in a noisy environment,
especially for those with reduced ability to discriminate speech

Products with speech output can be difficult to
understand if the ambient noise levels are loud

Hearing functions: Sound localisation

Sound localisation is the ability to tell the direction of a sound. A sound reaches one ear with a slightly higher intensity, and fractionally before it reaches the other ear, and the brain uses this information to work out where the sound is coming from. The ability to localise a sound therefore requires two functional ears, and this ability diminishes with performance reductions in either or both ears.

When sound localisation ability is low, it affects a person's safe interaction in an environment. For example, if a person cannot tell the direction of an approaching bus or a car, he or she could be in danger of being struck by the vehicle.

Sound localisation is important when interacting with products that use sound to warn the user, or indicate where they are. The localisation can be assisted by other outputs such as lights, motion or vibration.

The sound of an ambulance siren is difficult to localise, because it contains only two specific frequencies. White noise is the easiest to localise, as this has a broad frequency range.

Reduced sound localisation ability could lead to
fatal consequences in busy environments

Environmental context

The most important factor that affects hearing is the presence of noise. Noise is essentially the ambient sound environment that interferes with the perception of the sound of interest. Noise introduces hearing demands in that the user has to discriminate the sound of interest from a mixture of other sounds.

Spaces that introduce large amounts of reflection and reverberation of sound can cause problems with hearing. The sound becomes distorted and therefore more difficult to discriminate from the background noise. This occurs in public spaces where announcements are important, such as train and underground stations, sports arenas and music halls. Increased reverberation affects people of all abilities, but affects those with reduced ability to a greater extent.

Hearing aids are least effective in noisy environments, as they amplify the background noise indiscriminately. Induction or T-coil loops transmit sound directly to a hearing aid, which can be set to only receive this signal, thereby eliminating the background noise entirely.

The ability to understand announcements and speech
depends on the background noise level

Reverberation in large halls and public spaces
can make speech unintelligible

Design guidance

- Provide adjustable volume levels where possible, failing that, ensure sufficient loudness for the ambient noise level

- Ensure that the frequencies of beeps and tones are within the range 800 to 1000 Hz in order to maximise the number of people able to detect them

- Use natural recorded speech in preference to synthesised speech, and avoid high pitch speech

- Use intonation, an appropriate word rate and clear pronunciation to help speech recognition

- Think about assisting those with hearing impairments by supplementing information through visual or tactile means, with due consideration for information overload

- Think about enabling the user to customise the tone and volume of auditory outputs

- Consider using sounds that contain multiple frequencies to help people determine where the sound is coming from

- Think about providing inductive couplings to assist communication with hearing aids

- Contemplate sound reflection and reverberation when designing environments and spaces

- Ensure that systems that transmit and reproduce speech do so with sufficient clarity

Hearing

The phone has inductive couplers for hearing aids, while the crossing unit uses sound and light to alert the user, in addition to a vibrating cone underneath the unit

Systems that transmit speech need to do so with sufficient loudness and clarity

Population statistics: Prevalence data

Hearing ability level (in increasing order)

H1   Cannot hear sounds at all

H2   Cannot follow a TV programme with the volume turned up

H3   Has difficulty hearing someone talking in a loud voice in a quiet room

H4   Cannot hear a doorbell, alarm clock or telephone bell

H5   Cannot use the telephone

H6   Cannot follow a TV programme at a volume others find acceptable

H7   Has difficulty hearing someone talking in a normal voice in a quiet room

H8   Has great difficulty following a conversation against background noise

H9   Full hearing ability

Ability level is measured with any desired hearing aids.

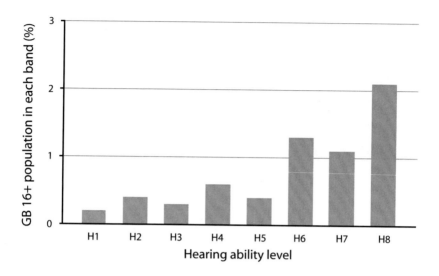

Graph showing the distribution of hearing ability,
where those with full ability (H9) are not shown

Important note

These ability levels and prevalence statistics are taken
directly from the 1996/97 Disability Follow-up Survey
(Grundy 1999), which was commissioned by the
government to plan welfare support. The GB adult
population was 45.6 million people at the time of the
survey. Please see the Framework section within Part 4:
User capabilities for more detail.

Grundy E, Ahlburg D, Ali M, Breeze E, Sloggett A (1999) Research
report 94 - Disability in Great Britain. Corporate Document Services,
London, UK. ISBN 1-84123-119-3.

Hearing

Population statistics: Demand & exclusion

No demand

- The user is not required to perceive anything by hearing

Low demand

The user is required to have sufficient ability to do things like

- Understand someone talking in a loud voice in a quiet room without difficulty

- Follow a TV programme with the volume turned up

Moderate demand

The user is required to have sufficient ability to do things like

- Understand someone talking over a normal telephone in a quiet room

- Notice a doorbell or alarm clock

High demand

The user is required to have sufficient ability to do things like

- Follow a conversation during background noise without great difficulty

- Follow a TV programme at a volume that others find acceptable

Demand levels assume that any desired hearing aids will be used.

Hearing

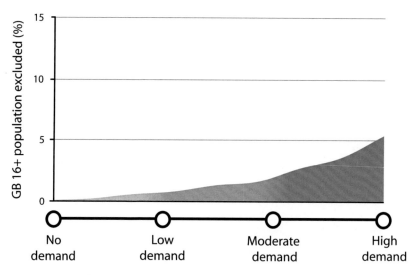

Graph showing the number of people who would be
excluded due to various levels of hearing demand

Important note

These statements refer to the level of hearing ability
that a product or service demands, in order to use it.
For a particular demand level, the 1996/97 Disability
Follow-up Survey is used to calculate the total number
of people who do not have this level of ability, and will
therefore be excluded. The GB adult population was
45.6 million people at the time of the survey. Please see
the Framework section within Part 4: User capabilities for
more detail.

Hearing

Thinking

Pat Langdon and Sam Waller

Overview

Thinking, also known as 'cognition', is the way we respond to sensory perceptions of the world, process them and choose our responses. We do this with continual reference to long-term memory, using a short-term memory area for mental working that is also linked to conscious attention.

The brain organises incoming sensory information, processes it in the light of consciousness through attention and then initiates responses in the form of actions. At a higher level, the sensory, cognitive and motor functions of thinking are integrated together within the brain. Understanding the interaction between these is a basis for good product design.

Thinking

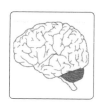 **Understanding thinking**

 **Cognitive processes**

 **Types of thinking**

 **Design guidance**

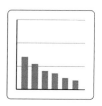 **Population statistics**

Thinking

Understanding thinking

Most of the processes that underlie thinking occur in the brain, which forms part of the central nervous system, which in turn transmits sensations and sends signals to muscles through the spinal cord and nerves.

Biological studies have shown that different regions of the brain are specifically involved in different cognitive functions such as: attention, memory, vision, hearing, and movement initiation as well as coordination and speech. Many functions are also dispersed throughout the brain.

With age there is a general slowing of intentional action and reduction in capability for attention. The ability to recognize patterns is also reduced. There is an increased susceptibility to distraction whilst attending to a task, resulting in reduced capability for tasks that require two or more simultaneous functions.

Well-established memories and skills are unaffected with age, whereas the time required to learn new things, make decisions and respond to sensory information increases, as can the frequency of errors.

Degenerative brain disorders are more prevalent with age, examples of which include Parkinson's and Alzheimer's diseases. These affect memory, attention, movement, perception, reasoning and social interaction to varying degrees.

Thinking

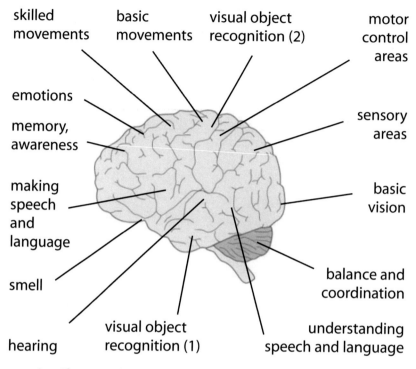

skilled movements

basic movements

visual object recognition (2)

motor control areas

emotions

memory, awareness

sensory areas

making speech and language

basic vision

smell

balance and coordination

hearing

visual object recognition (1)

understanding speech and language

Specific areas of the brain are known to be involved in different functions, although other functions are dispersed throughout the brain

Thinking

Cognitive processes: Introduction

The brain serves many functions, a complete description of which are beyond the scope of this text. For understanding product interaction, the following are most significant

- Perceiving involves processing to convert low-level senses, such as light, shade and colour, into high-level perceptions, such as objects, faces and an overall understanding of the environment

- Working memory describes the temporary storage used to process and rearrange all information with reference to perceptions of the current environment and long-term stored memories

- Long-term memory describes the processes through which information encountered repeatedly in working memory can be learnt, stored indefinitely, and retrieved

- Thinking includes attention, which refers to the function of working memory; visual thinking, which refers to the understanding and mental manipulation of visual information in the current environment; and verbal thinking, which refers to the conversion of speech, words and symbols into language, and the use of language to store and categorise memories

- Acting involves processing to convert general intentions and movements into specific actions, in the form of sequenced instructions to muscles

Thinking

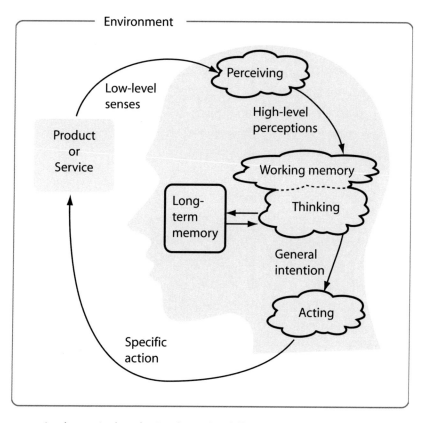

A schematic that depicts how the different processes involved
with thinking relate to each other and to a product in the world

Cognitive processes: Perceiving

Perceiving is the process by which the brain represents and interprets the information signals sent by the body's sensory system. Sensory information is available from the eyes (vision); from the ears (hearing, balance) and from the skin, muscles and skeleton (touch, body-sense) for the brain to process into sounds, objects and surfaces, leading to an understanding of the current environment.

Low-level sensory information is briefly stored, while processing distinguishes and selects important features. For visual processing, information about shading, colour, motion and depth may be used to separate shapes from their background and identify objects. Recognition occurs when higher-level cognitive visual processing groups features into edges, clusters and patterns, then rotates and scales the image to match items in memory.

Some aspects of the environment may be perceived automatically, such as the use of light and shadow to form a perception of a three-dimensional object. Visual illusions highlight instances where alternative interpretations of the perceived environment are possible.

Working memory allows us to reason about visual features and spatial relationships. Similar processing and representations are also involved in hearing to enable us to perceive speech, and to detect sounds in noisy environments. Our sense of where the body is within the environment results from the coordinated operation of all senses.

Thinking

4-78

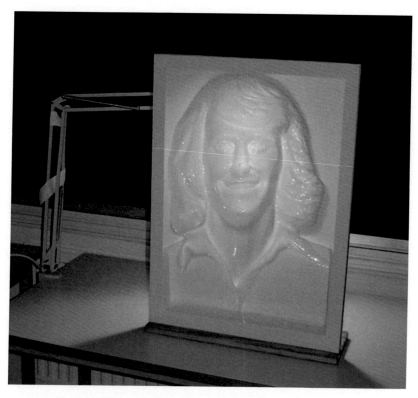

The face on this mould is actually sticking out backwards from the page, but visual processing misinterprets the light and shadow to form a mental construction where the face sticks out forwards

Image source: Wikimedia commons

Cognitive processes: Working memory

Working memory is used to manipulate and rearrange information within the span of attention. Information can originate from memory or from perception, and can be stored for up to 20 seconds before it decays. Information can be held in different forms, such as the verbal meaning of words (e.g a word 'house'), the visual or spatial content of attended material (e.g. 'the shape of a house') or its episodic context (e. g. 'it's the place where I live').

Attention and executive function refers to the execution of the processes that interface between long-term memory, working memory, perception and cognition; the number of different things that can be kept in working memory at once; and the choice and focus of information that is processed.

Working memory is known to be organised into 'chunks' or items. This type of memory can be thought of as a rough working area for items being attended to. Examples of its use include remembering a phone number that's being read out, or a list of words presented in a drop down menu, or where the objects on a table are in relation to each other.

The capacity of working memory is known to be limited to around 7 chunks or items, although the amount of information that can actually be simultaneously stored and processed depends on the form of the information, the way in which it is chunked together, and how the present information links together and with stored memories.

Thinking

Working memory is involved in the awareness of where objects are in relation to each other, and in the temporary storage of numbers

Cognitive processes: Long-term memory

Long-term memories require learning and repetition to become fixed, but once stored they can last a long time and be retrieved by triggers or cues. Knowledge may be in different forms, such as remembering what things are; how to do something; or remembering linked episodes of verbal and visual interactions that occurred in the past. Prospective memory is remembering to do something in the future, such as checking that food left cooking is not burning.

Remembering that the perceptual cues in front of you are similar to a stored memory is called recognition, while remembering something stored in memory from different cues in front of you is called recall. Identifying whether you have seen someone's face before requires recognition, while remembering their name takes longer because it requires recall.

Our general prior experience helps to realise that buttons should be pushed, and handles should be pulled, while specific experience with a product makes it easier to use in the future. The ability to use a new product is strongly dependent on how well it matches with these specific and general experiences. Our ability to learn decreases with age, so a product is likely to be difficult to use for an older person if it does not match up with their experiences when younger. Initial interaction with an unfamiliar product is characterised by frequent errors but this can improve if the product supports learning through feedback.

The shape and form of these doors suggests how they should be opened

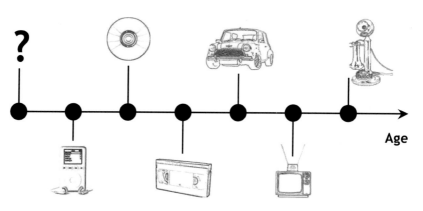

People of different ages have different experience backgrounds, and in most cases the user's past experiences will be different to the designers

Types of thinking: Introduction

The different processes involved with thinking include

- Attention, which is the way in which the mind allows conscious selective attention to specific things in the environment, affects awareness of the environment by filtering out non-attended things and can sometimes be 'grabbed' unconsciously by salient or intrusive events

- Visual thinking, which is the ability to perceive and think about visual objects and spatial relationships in two and three dimensions

- Verbal thinking, which refers to the conversion of speech, words and symbols into language, and also the use of established knowledge stored as episodes and categories in long-term memory

Interaction with memory is critical for the processes involved with thinking.

Attention is the way in which the mind allows conscious
selective attention to specific things in the environment

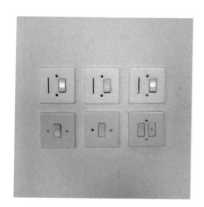 

Visual-spatial thinking is required to relate the switches
on a wall to the lights that they control

Types of thinking: Attention

Attention is thought to be a function of working memory. It can be consciously directed towards specific tasks, or it can be 'grabbed' by a distracting event such as a flashing light or the sound of one's name. This can be advantageous, to direct a persons attention towards a warning or impending hazard, or can be a distraction if a flashing light disrupts attention away from the task at hand.

For each individual, attention can be overloaded if too many things have to be kept in mind at once, in which case items or tasks may be forgotten. For example, if a person attempts to cook while having a conversation or reading, it is likely that something will be forgotten or an action will be missed.

Working memory performance is also affected by the time taken to process incoming sensory information, and to decide on, and implement, the required response. For example, when driving a car, incoming sensory information is continually processed in the form of road hazards, signs, and information from the vehicle. If the user cannot process and respond to the incoming information fast enough, then newly arriving information passes unnoticed, or existing information is lost.

Working memory has limited overall resources which are divided amongst separate visual and verbal modes, each of which use their own storage.

Using products such as car stereos while driving imposes
additional load onto attentional resources

Driving a car adds time pressure to crucial decisions,
such as whether to turn off on a slip road

Types of thinking: Visual thinking

Visual thinking is the ability to perceive and think about visual objects and spatial relationships in two and three dimensions. Some key functions are

- Filtering and extracting information from the low-level sensory information the eyes receive, to identify and group objects

- Relating objects and icons to each other according to their spatial position, for example understanding the relationship between the control knobs and the burner positions on a cooker

- Rotating drawings, symbols or text in two dimensions, or objects in three dimensions

- Grouping objects according to properties such as their shape, colour or spatial alignment

Visual thinking and other processes develop a perception of shape, using colour, shading, depth and motion. Shapes are then matched to objects in our visual memories. Buttons that share similar functions on a calculator have been designed so that they are perceived as part of the same visual group, thereby making the calculator easier to use.

Careful inspection of this cooker top shows a subtle visual link between each knob and the corresponding burner, thereby reducing the spatial ability required to use it

Types of thinking: Verbal thinking

Verbal thinking refers to the conversion of speech, words and symbols into meaningful constructs, and the use of established semantic knowledge (what things are) stored in long term memory.

Semantic memory holds words and their meanings, the relationships between words and more complex structures such as language, grammar, rules and knowledge. These elements are constructed and utilised through processes of relating, reasoning, and categorising that are thought to be carried out in working memory as a result of executive processing.

In order to understand speech and printed material, low-level auditory and visual processing must first separate the sounds and letters from the background. Higher-level processing, under the control of attention, can then operate on the word sounds and text objects to generate words that are held in working memory. These processes use separate auditory and visual stores.

Executive processes in working memory then interface with long-term memory to enable the meaning of words to be understood. Retrieved episodic memories further contextualise how, where and when these words were encountered. High-level thinking can then use memories of how to do things to generate speech or writing by the initiation of low-level muscular actions.

The icons on the fax machine are reinforced by accompanying text, whereas those on the photocopier are not

A message that uses simple language and gives information in multiple forms is preferable to one that assumes a high level of language skills

Design guidance: Perception and attention

- Use shapes, colours and alignment to assist visual grouping of features that share some kind of similarity, thereby reducing the time and working memory required to locate a desired feature

- Align controls in a spatial orientation that matches the devices they affect, or provide an obvious link between controls and the corresponding devices

- Consider the increased demand on spatial ability if left and right are used to represent up and down (or vice versa), and avoid this situation wherever possible

- Use the visual form of the device to help users understand what areas they can interact with, and the correct way to interact with them

- Try to use simple language, and supplement textual information with images and icons

- Be wary of potential problems that can result if multiple actions have to be completed within a certain time period

- Try to ensure that attention is only required to be directed in one place at any one time

Thinking

A cooker top that has its controls aligned in a spatial orientation which matches the corresponding devices, compared to one that does not

The shape and form of this door does not help the user understand how it should be opened

Design guidance: Memory and learning

- Use structure to assist memory and learning

- Reduce the number of information chunks that need to be kept in mind at any given time, and try not to exceed 5 as the best practice

- Where hierarchy is used, ensure the current location within the overall hierarchy is always evident and try not to exceed three levels

- Assist learning and recall through distinctive spatial positions for menu options, and be wary of the potential confusion if these positions change

- Provide an obvious mechanism that allows users to get back to their previous location or home when navigating any menu structure

- Consider the memory implication of unseen content if scrolling is required to obtain more menu items

- Support learning by ensuring that all possible actions generate suitable feedback that guides the user

- Try to ensure all actions are easily and immediately reversible, and try to constrain the availability of actions that would result in undesirable or irreversible outcomes

Thinking

Helpful feedback is provided if the user attempts to press
buttons while the keylock on this phone is active

Thinking

Population statistics: Prevalence data

Thinking ability level
The ability level is calculated using this table, which considers the number of disabilities from the list below

T1	11 disabilities	T7	5 disabilities
T2	10 disabilities	T8	4 disabilities
T3	9 disabilities	T9	3 disabilities
T4	8 disabilities	T10	2 disabilities
T5	7 disabilities	T11	1 disability
T6	6 disabilities	T12	Full thinking ability

Thinking disabilities
- Often loses track of what is being said in the middle of a conversation
- Thoughts tend to be muddled or slow
- Often gets confused about what time of day it is
- Cannot watch a 30 minute TV programme all the way through, and tell someone what it was about
- Cannot read a short newspaper article
- Cannot write a short letter to someone without help
- Cannot count well enough to handle money
- Cannot remember a message and pass it on correctly
- Often forgets to turn things off, such as fires, cookers or taps
- Often forgets the names of friends and family that are seen regularly
- Often forgets what was supposed to be doing in the middle of something

Thinking

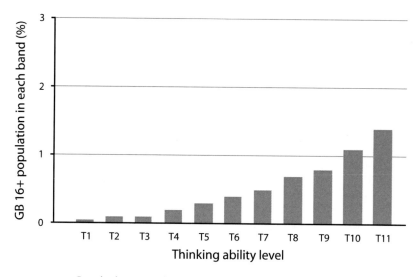

Graph showing the distribution of thinking ability,
where those with full ability (T12) are not shown

Important note

These ability levels and prevalence statistics are taken directly from the 1996/97 Disability Follow-up Survey (Grundy 1999), which was commissioned by the government to plan welfare support. The GB adult population was 45.6 million people at the time of the survey. Please see the Framework section within Part 4: User capabilities for more detail.

Thinking

Grundy E, Ahlburg D, Ali M, Breeze E, Sloggett A (1999) Research report 94 - Disability in Great Britain. Corporate Document Services, London, UK. ISBN 1-84123-119-3.

Population statistics: Demand & exclusion

No demand
The user is not required to do things similar to any of the tasks listed below

Low demand
The user is required to do things similar to 4 of the tasks below

Moderate demand
The user is required to do things similar to 7 of the tasks below

High demand
The user is required to do things similar to 11 of the tasks below

Thinking tasks
- Hold a conversation without losing track of what is being said
- Think clearly, without muddling thoughts
- Tell the time of day, without any confusion
- Watch a 30 minute TV programme, and tell someone what it was about
- Read a short newspaper article
- Write a short letter to someone without help
- Count well enough to handle money
- Remember a message and pass it on correctly
- Remember to turn things off, such as fires, cookers or taps
- Remember the names of friends and family that are seen regularly
- Do something without forgetting what the task was whilst in the middle of it

Thinking

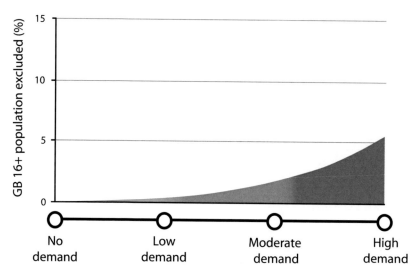

Graph showing the number of people who would be
excluded due to various levels of thinking demand

Important note

These statements refer to the level of thinking ability
that a product or service demands, in order to use it.
For a particular demand level, the 1996/97 Disability
Follow-up Survey is used to calculate the total number
of people who do not have this level of ability, and will
therefore be excluded. The GB adult population was
45.6 million people at the time of the survey. Please see
the Framework section within Part 4: User capabilities for
more detail.

Communication

Pat Langdon and Sam Waller

Understanding a person's ability to communicate with devices or people in their environment requires extensive consideration of language. For the purposes of product design, communication is assumed to be the capability to understand or express simple sentences in speech or text. This is primarily a result of thinking in general, and in particular verbal thinking. It also involves visual thinking, memory, attention, vision and hearing.

A product interface makes a communication demand on the user. Text and speech can describe what controls do, provide feedback, issue warnings or commands, and provide detailed instructions. Usability is therefore dependent on the capability to

- Perceive and understand written words and sentences on their own or in the context of a more complex environment

- Perceive and understand spoken words and sentences in both quiet and noisy environments

Educational level and social skills will influence a person's communication ability, and therefore affect product interaction.

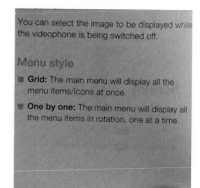

You can select the image to be displayed while the videophone is being switched off.

Menu style

■ **Grid:** The main menu will display all the menu items/icons at once.

■ **One by one:** The main menu will display all the menu items in rotation, one at a time.

Understanding a single word on a button is easier than understanding the meaning of sentences

Further details

Visual and non-verbal communication

Here, the main concern is with linguistic communication in speech, writing, words and sentences. Other types of communication include visual, iconic or symbolic messages, or non-linguistic sounds and gestures. Successful product design requires careful consideration of the many alternative types of communication.

Impairment and communication

Communication can be affected by impairment of the functions necessary for communicating.

- Hearing impairments can cause difficulties with under-standing verbal communication, and also generating speech

- Visual impairments will affect the ability to read, and to interpret lip movements. They also affect the ability to detect and interpret other non-verbal communications that accompany speech

- Cognitive impairments can affect the quality and quantity of linguistic capability

- Language impairments may include a reduced vocab-ulary, or a poor understanding of words and grammar

In addition, variation in language skills across the population results in the need to accommodate a wide spectrum of vocabulary and competency in grammar when designing products. For more information on communication and language, see Harley (2001)

for more than 5 minutes before washing.

● After use, turn the pink nozzle to the 'OFF' position.

CAUTION

Irritating to eyes. Keep out of reach of children. Avoid contact with eyes. In case of contact with eyes, rinse immediately with plenty of water and seek medical advice. If swallowed, seek medical advice immediately and show this container or label.

IRRITANT

Vanish Spray contains amongst other ingredients: 5-15% Non-ionic surfactants. Contains: Perfume, Hexyl Cinnamal, Citronellol, Preservatives (Methylchloroisothiazolinone; Methylisothiazolinone).   www.rbeuroinfo.com

Vanish™ Consumer Services For help and advice, contact us: www.vanish.co.uk

Successful product design requires careful consideration of the many alternative types of communication

Communication

Harley T (2001) The Psychology of Language: From Data to Theory. Psychology Press, Hove, UK

Population statistics: Prevalence data

Communication ability level (in increasing order)

C1   Is impossible for people who know him/her well to understand. Finds it impossible to understand people who know him/her well

C2   Is impossible for strangers to understand. Is very difficult for people who know him/her well to understand. Finds it impossible to understand strangers. Finds it very difficult to understand people who know him/her well

C3   Is very difficult for strangers to understand. Is quite difficult for people who know him/her well to understand. Finds it difficult to understand strangers. Finds it quite difficult to understand people who know him/her well

C4   Is quite difficult for strangers to understand. Finds it quite difficult to understand strangers

C5   Other people have some difficulty understanding him/her. Has some difficulty understanding what other people say or what they mean

C6   Full communication ability

Ability levels refer to a person communicating with others who speak the same language

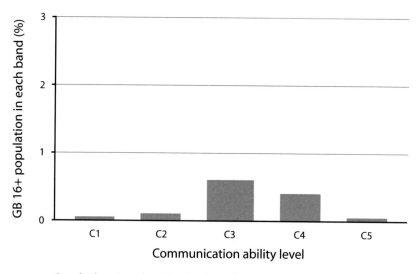

Graph showing the distribution of communication ability, where those with full ability (C6) are not shown

Important note

These ability levels and prevalence statistics are taken directly from the 1996/97 Disability Follow-up Survey (Grundy 1999), which was commissioned by the government to plan welfare support. The GB adult population was 45.6 million people at the time of the survey. Please see the Framework section within Part 4: User capabilities for more detail.

Communication

Grundy E, Ahlburg D, Ali M, Breeze E, Sloggett A (1999) Research report 94 - Disability in Great Britain. Corporate Document Services, London, UK. ISBN 1-84123-119-3.

Population statistics: Demand & exclusion

No demand

- The user is not required to communicate with other people

Low demand

The user is required to have sufficient ability to do things like

- Understand, or express themselves to strangers (albeit with extreme difficulty)

- Understand, or express themselves to well known people (albeit with some difficulty)

Moderate demand

The user is required to have sufficient ability to do things like

- Understand, or express themselves to strangers (albeit with some difficulty)

- Understand, or express themselves to well known people (easily)

High demand

The user is required to have sufficient ability to do things like

- Understand, or express themselves to strangers (easily)

Demand levels assume the user is communicating with others who speak the same language

Communication

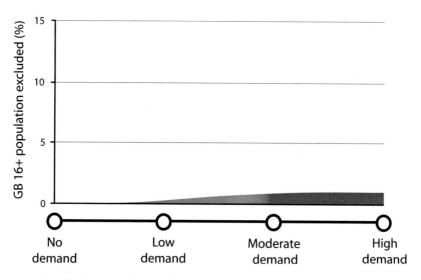

Graph showing the number of people who would be excluded
due to various levels of communication demand

Important note

These statements refer to the level of communication
ability that a product or service demands, in order to use
it. For a particular demand level, the 1996/97 Disability
Follow-up Survey is used to calculate the total number
of people who do not have this level of ability, and will
therefore be excluded. The GB adult population was
45.6 million people at the time of the survey. Please see
the Framework section within Part 4: User capabilities for
more detail.

Communication

Locomotion

Umesh Persad and Carlos Cardoso

Overview

Locomotion is the ability to move and walk around in the environment. Activities such as walking, getting in and out of vehicles, moving on and off furniture and maintaining balance are affected by loss of locomotion ability.

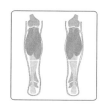 **Understanding locomotion**

 **Locomotion functions**

 **Environmental context**

 **Design guidance**

 **Population statistics**

Locomotion

Understanding locomotion

In order to move around, we require adequate muscle strength, motor control and balance. Locomotion includes the ability to sit down and stand up, to get up and down from the floor, and to move around in an environment by walking and ascending or descending steps.

Muscle strength gradually deteriorates with age, while degenerative conditions such as arthritis and Parkinson's disease further limit joint mobility and muscle control. The arms are also more likely to be employed to compensate for impairment of strength and balance.

The reduction in visual ability with age also causes problems with moving around an environment. Coupled with reduced muscular strength, it can be difficult for older and disabled people to move around with speed and agility.

Temporary loss of locomotion ability can also occur due to sprained ankles, knee problems, or falls. A sudden loss of locomotion ability may be caused by lower limb amputation, immobilisation, or a stroke. While intense training and assistive devices can help to gradually improve locomotion ability, a return to full function is unlikely.

Locomotion

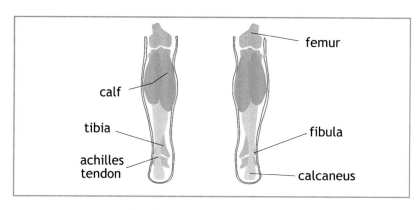

The shape and structure of legs

Locomotion functions: Walking

Gait refers to the manner of walking and it has unique aspects apparent in each person. It is cyclic involving repeated movements of the lower and upper limbs, and also of the trunk.

Normal gait is rhythmic and characterised by alternating forward and backward motion, and weight transfer between the lower limbs. The characteristics of the gait cycle are directly affected by the speed of movement, the evenness of the ground, body weight, body symmetry, and age and health status.

During normal walking, up to 85% of the person's weight may need to be supported by one lower limb. Each leg supports weight for approximately 64% of the cycle, and swings free for the remaining 36%. Running is characterized by periods when both feet are off the ground, and therefore requires greater strength, joint mobility and balance.

As strength, mobility or balance decrease people tend to take shorter steps and reduce the time for which only one leg supports weight. Walking aids allow the arms to help with balance and weight support. This improves walking speed and stamina for those with limited strength and mobility while a wheelchair can assist those whose capability is further impaired.

For more information on walking, see Rose (1994)

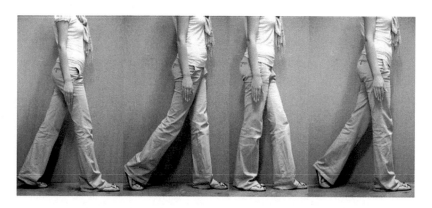

Positions of the legs during a gait cycle for normal walking

Examples of locomotion aids

Rose J and Gamble JG (1994) Human Walking. Williams & Wilkins, Baltimore USA.

Locomotion functions: Getting around

Climbing stairs is cyclic in a similar manner to walking, but requires increased strength, mobility and balance. It is therefore more likely that the person will need to use their arms to help assist. Climbing steps is impossible for those in wheelchairs, and can be particularly challenging for many others because walking aids such as sticks and trolleys are no longer effective.

Actions such as bending down to the floor or squatting, sitting down, standing up, or getting into and out of confined spaces can also be very difficult for people with low locomotion ability.

Reducing the muscle strength and flexibility required to use a product or to move around in an environment helps to include those with reduced locomotion capability. This can be achieved through careful use of dimensions and shapes and making extra allowance for the hands to help move the body around.

Locomotion

Climbing stairs is easier if hand rails are provided
to assist strength and balance

Getting out of a seat is easier if the upper body can assist

Locomotion

Environmental context

The provision of a suitable environment can dramatically affect those with reduced locomotion capability, who often use various aids such as walking sticks, crutches, frames and trolleys, wheelchairs and scooters in order to increase their mobility.

Product and environmental design should factor the use of these aids into design solutions. Eliminating steps and space constrictions to help wheelchair users results in designs that benefit others, such as people with push-chairs, bicycles, or suitcases on wheels.

Balance aids are essential in transportation situations such as buses and trains, but can also reduce design exclusion and increase user satisfaction in any situation involving standing for long periods, such as queuing.

Environments should provide adequate capability for people to rest while getting from one place to another. Regular seating intervals can also be useful for those carrying heavy bags, or who want to rest or tie-up their shoelaces.

Locomotion

Ramps can help provide access for all users,
especially those using mobility aids

Balance aids are useful in transport environments, and in
any situation involving standing for long periods

Design guidance

- Consider the use of locomotion aids such as walkers, wheelchairs and scooters when setting the dimensions of doorways and passages

- Provide adequate seating at regular intervals in public spaces such as parks, airports and shopping centres

- Provide handles or surfaces so that the arms can be used to assist transferring the body between different positions (such as sitting and standing)

- Reduce the need to bend the back or reach below waist level

- Assist balance by ensuring that something is available to hold on to, especially for any situation involving steps, or standing for a long period

- Be wary of the exclusion that results from requiring the user to ascend even one step

- Ensure that devices to assist locomotion are integrated with the overall design aesthetic

Locomotion

Provision of adequate seating at regular intervals
is important for public spaces

Large doors on taxis allow easier access, and many buses can
be lowered to curb level making them easier to enter

Population statistics: Prevalence data

Locomotion ability level (in increasing order)

L1 Cannot walk at all

L2 Can only walk a few steps without stopping or severe discomfort. Cannot walk up and down one step

L3 Has fallen 12 or more times in the last year

L4 Always needs to hold on to something to keep balance

L5 Cannot walk up and down a flight of 12 stairs

L6 Cannot walk 50 yds without stopping or severe discomfort

L7 Cannot bend down far enough to touch knees and straighten up again

L8 Cannot bend down and pick up something from the floor and straighten up again

L9 Cannot walk 200 yds without stopping or severe discomfort. Can only walk up and down a flight of 12 stairs if holds on and takes a rest. Often needs to hold on to something to keep balance. Has fallen 3 or more times in the last year

L10 Can only walk up and down a flight of twelve stairs if holds on (doesn't need a rest)

L11 Cannot bend down to sweep up something from the floor and straighten up again

L12 Can only walk up and down a flight of stairs if goes sideways or one step at a time

L13 Cannot walk 400 yds without stopping or severe discomfort

L14 Full locomotion ability

Ability level is measured with any desired walking aids, but without anyone else's assistance. Ability to bend down is measured with something available to hold on to

Locomotion

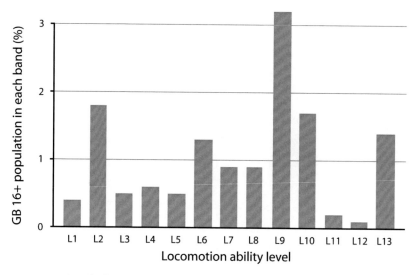

Graph showing the distribution of locomotion ability,
where those with full ability (L14) are not shown

Important note

These ability levels and prevalence statistics are taken
directly from the 1996/97 Disability Follow-up Survey
(Grundy 1999), which was commissioned by the
government to plan welfare support. The GB adult
population was 45.6 million people at the time of the
survey. Please see the Framework section within Part 4:
User capabilities for more detail.

Grundy E, Ahlburg D, Ali M, Breeze E, Sloggett A (1999) Research
report 94 - Disability in Great Britain. Corporate Document Services,
London, UK. ISBN 1-84123-119-3.

Locomotion

Population statistics: Demand & exclusion

No demand

- The user is not required to walk or use steps, or to balance on own for any period, or to perform any bending tasks

Low demand

The user is required to have sufficient ability to do things like
- Walk 50 metres (≈ 50 yds) without stopping
- Ascend or descend a flight of 12 stairs on own, using a handrail and resting; or balance for short periods without holding on to something
- Bend down far enough to touch knees, and then straighten up again

Moderate demand

The user is required to have sufficient ability to do things like
- Walk 175 metres (≈ 200 yds) without stopping
- Ascend or descend a flight of 12 stairs on own, without rests (but using a handrail); or balance for long periods without holding on to something
- Bend down to pick something up from the floor, and then straighten up again

High demand

The user is required to have sufficient ability to do things like
- Walk 350 metres (≈ 400 yds) without stopping
- Ascend or descend a flight of 12 steps on own, without handrails and without resting
- Bend down to use a dustpan and brush, and then straighten up again

Locomotion

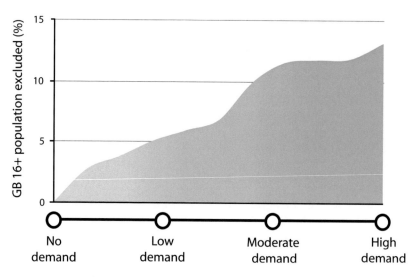

Graph showing the number of people who would be
excluded due to various levels of locomotion demand

Important note

These statements refer to the level of locomotion ability
that a product or service demands, in order to use it.
For a particular demand level, the 1996/97 Disability
Follow-up Survey is used to calculate the total number
of people who do not have this level of ability, and will
therefore be excluded. The GB adult population was
45.6 million people at the time of the survey. Please see
the Framework section within Part 4: User capabilities for
more detail.

**Walking demands assume that any desired walking aids will be
used, but no-one else is assisting. Bending demands assume that
something is available to hold on to.**

Reach & stretch

Umesh Persad and Carlos Cardoso

Overview

Reach & stretch covers the ability for one or both arms to reach out in front, above the head, or behind the back.

 **Understanding reach & stretch**

 **Reach & stretch functions**

 **Environmental context**

 **Design guidance**

 **Population statistics**

Understanding reach & stretch

Different products require the ability to reach one or both arms out from the body. This reaching can either occur in front of and above the body (to put on a hat), or out to the sides (to reach objects while sitting at a desk).

Reaching becomes more difficult as the arm moves further away from the rest position or when two arms have to reach out simultaneously.

The relative ability to position the hands compared to the head and body depends on the range of motion of the elbow and shoulder joints. The absolute position that each hand can reach to is also influenced by ergonomic factors such as body height and arm length, together with considerations such as wheelchair use.

Age-related conditions such as arthritis can cause reductions in joint mobility and stiffness leading to limited reaching ability. The distance that people can reach out to might be significantly less than the length of their arms.

Temporary injuries such as a broken or bruised arm or collarbone will also affect the distance a person can reach to.

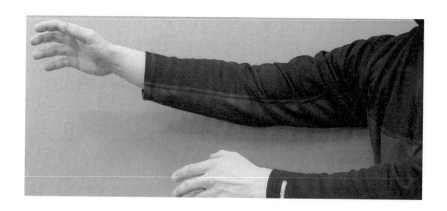

 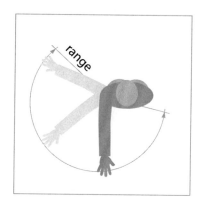

The shape and movement of arms

Reach & stretch functions

For product interaction, reach & stretch ability can be broken down into the ability to move one or both arms in two perpendicular directions, as shown in the figures opposite.

Most products require the ability to put one hand in front of the body to use them. Where possible, requiring both hands to be placed in front of the body simultaneously should be avoided. Using products should be possible by reaching either the left or right arm. Requiring people to reach above their heads is more demanding than requiring them to reach out in front.

Reaching out to the sides is used to access items while sitting at a desk, or to put on a jacket. The further the arm has to reach out to the side or back, the more difficult it can be to reach items.

A person's range of motion is characterised by the ability
to reach out in front, above the head and to the sides

Environmental context

Environmental factors can additionally reduce a person's reach & stretch capability.

- **Carrying things** while using a product will reduce the mobility of one or both hands, and it may not be desirable for the user to have to put down things such as tools, handbags or carrier bags

- **Clothing** such as heavy jackets and multiple layers can reduce a person's ability and comfort to reach out

The context of use may restrict the ability to move one or both arms

The ability to reach may be restricted by heavy clothing

Design guidance

- Provide the option to operate a product by either reaching out the left or right arm, and try to avoid requiring both arms to be reached out at the same time

- Ensure that products or services requiring public access are able to cope with the range of heights that people can reach to, including those in wheelchairs

- Avoid requiring users to reach above their head, where possible, and note that the ability to exert forces will be greatly diminished when the arms are in this position

- Consult ergonomic data sources such as Tilley (2002) to help set the dimensions of products and environments

A variety of heights can account for the needs of different users

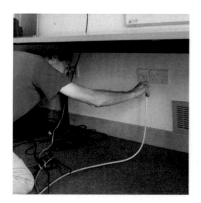

Providing plug sockets above desks makes
them significantly easier to reach

Tilley AR (2002) The Measure of Man and Woman, John Wiley & Sons,
New York, USA. ISBN 0-471-09955-4

Reach & stretch

Population statistics: Prevalence data

Reach & stretch ability level (in increasing order)

R1   Cannot hold out either arm in front to shake hands

R2   Cannot put either arm up to head to put a hat on

R3   Cannot put either hand behind back to put jacket on or tuck shirt in

R4   Cannot raise either arm above head to reach for something

R5   Has difficulty holding either arm in front to shake hands with someone

R6   Has difficulty putting either arm up to head to put a hat on

R7   Has difficulty putting either hand behind back to put jacket on or tuck shirt in

R8   Has difficulty raising either arm above head to reach for something

R9   Cannot hold one arm out in front or up to head (but can with other arm)

R10 Cannot put one arm behind back to put on jacket or tuck shirt in (but can with other arm). Has difficulty putting one arm behind back to put jacket on or tuck shirt in, or putting one arm out in front or up to head (but no difficulty with other arm)

R11 Full reach & stretch ability

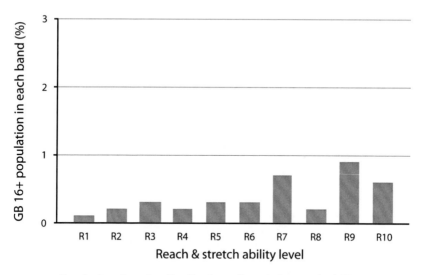

Graph showing the distribution of reach & stretch ability,
where those with full ability (R11) are not shown

Important note

These ability levels and prevalence statistics are taken
directly from the 1996/97 Disability Follow-up Survey
(Grundy 1999), which was commissioned by the
government to plan welfare support. The GB adult
population was 45.6 million people at the time of the
survey. Please see the Framework section within Part 4:
User capabilities for more detail.

Grundy E, Ahlburg D, Ali M, Breeze E, Sloggett A (1999) Research
report 94 - Disability in Great Britain. Corporate Document Services,
London, UK. ISBN 1-84123-119-3.

Reach & stretch

Population statistics: Demand & exclusion

No demand

- The user is not required to reach out with either arm

Low demand

The user is required to have sufficient ability to do things like

- Hold one arm out in front, up to the head, or behind the back (albeit with difficulty)

Moderate demand

The user is required to have sufficient ability to do things like

- Hold one arm out in front, up to the head, or behind the back (easily)

High demand

The user is required to have sufficient ability to do things like

- Hold both arms out in front, up to the head, or behind the back (easily)

Reach & stretch

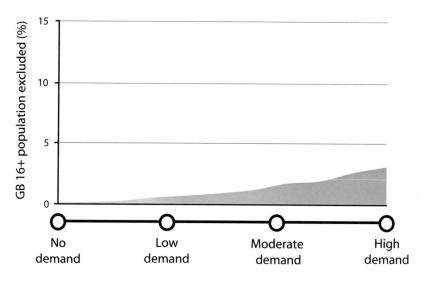

Graph showing the number of people who would be excluded
due to various levels of reach & stretch demand

Important note

These statements refer to the level of reach & stretch
ability that a product or service demands, in order to use
it. For a particular demand level, the 1996/97 Disability
Follow-up Survey is used to calculate the total number
of people who do not have this level of ability, and will
therefore be excluded. The GB adult population was
45.6 million people at the time of the survey. Please see
the Framework section within Part 4: User capabilities for
more detail.

Reach & stretch

Dexterity

Umesh Persad and Sam Waller

Overview

Dexterity covers the ability to grasp and hold objects, and to perform fine finger movements to manipulate small objects.

 **Understanding dexterity**

 **Dexterity functions**

 **Environmental context**

 **Design guidance**

 **Population statistics**

Dexterity

Understanding dexterity

Most products require physical manipulation of controls and manual handling. The hands are used to grasp, move and exert forces to use and operate various products. Objects can be grasped, pushed and pulled. The human hand is composed of four fingers and an opposable thumb, which is key to many dexterity tasks.

We can exert clamping forces between fingers and also clamp and hold larger objects in the palm of the hand. Individual fingers can be used to exert pulling and pushing forces. We often use both hands at the same time to manipulate objects. This coordinated movement requires strength and dexterity in the fingers together with sensory capability and motor control.

There are many causes of pain that can limit dexterity. Arthritis is one example that is particularly prevalent for older people, causing stiffness, swelling and pain in the joints. The satisfaction level for using a product is seriously affected when it causes pain, even if the product is still usable.

Many able bodied people will experience temporary bruising or breakages that can affect their dexterity capability. This causes particular frustration when attempting to use products that require unusually high levels of strength or two-handed co-ordination.

Dexterity

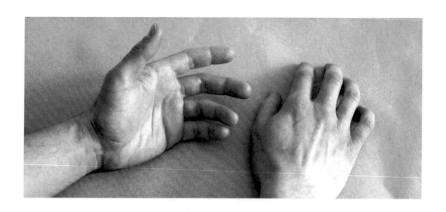

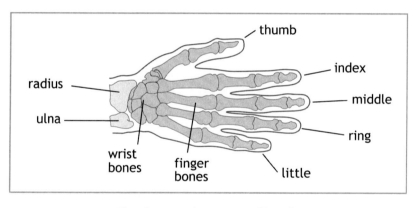

The shape and structure of hands

Dexterity functions: Introduction

The most critical dexterity functions for product interaction are now considered. A single hand can be used to generate a

- Push force using any part of the hand

- Pinch grip using the index finger and thumb to generate opposing forces

- Power grip using the palm and thumb together with all four fingers

A push force requires the least amount of dexterity capability because there is no need for an opposing grip. Two-handed tasks require the use of both hands to perform a combination of pushing or gripping. One hand is often required to hold or stabilise the object, while the other performs fine precision movements.

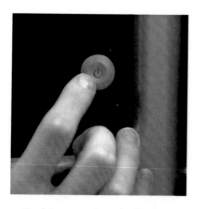

Pushing requires the lowest dexterity capability whereas holding and lifting a Scrabble piece requires a pinch grip with relatively low force

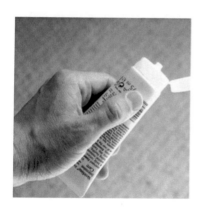

Squeezing cylindrical products requires a power grip, whereas opening a bottle requires both pinch and power grips

Dexterity functions: Pushing

The simplest dexterity function is when the fingers or palm are used to exert forces without grasping. The movement and force are aligned in the same direction, so there is no requirement for a friction contact. There are three possible perpendicular directions in which a force can be applied.

Large forces can be achieved by using the body weight to help push away from the body, for example when opening a door. If the surface to be pushed is vertical, then either the palm of the hand must be aligned with the vertical surface, or the fingers must be used to transmit the force. Both of these can be a source of pain. The pushing force can be generated more comfortably if the surface is contoured to fit the hand with a neutral wrist position.

Pushing up and down is used to depress buttons and sliders, such as that required for a toaster. It is more comfortable to push down than up, because the wrist has to rotate 180 degrees if the palm is required to push upwards.

Pushing left or right can be required to push a button on the side of a product, or to push a product from side to side. It is easier to push things towards the body centre-line rather than away from it, because this wrist position is more natural.

The simplest dexterity function is when the fingers or palm are used to exert forces without grasping

Pushing forces can be generated more comfortably if the surface allows for a neutral wrist position

Dexterity functions: Pinch gripping

Pinch gripping is the ability to develop opposable forces between the thumb and fingers of the hand. Pinch grips are often used to manipulate controls such as sliders and knobs, which only require minimal forces. Pinch grips should not generally be used to generate large forces. Instead, more hand muscles can be employed by a power grip, thereby increasing the strength that can be brought to bear.

Careful provision of shape and surface texture of controls should allow the user to operate the product with a loose grip formed with his or her preferred combination of thumb and fingers.

The maximum rotational force that can be generated by a pinch grip is dependent on the size and shape of the object to be turned. Circular objects such as door knobs are the hardest to grip and turn as the fingers tend to slip on the surface. The best shape for pinch grip turning allows the thumb and fingers to grasp either side of long strip.

Satisfying products can be operated with a loose grip, and both of these controls could be manipulated with alternative grips

Frustrating products require a tight pinch grip to operate, and the shape and texture on these controls are not well suited to the forces required

Dexterity functions: Power gripping

A power grip is formed with the thumb, all four fingers, and the palm of the hand. The large number of muscles used means that large forces can be generated with comparatively little effort, although the precision is reduced when compared to a pinch grip.

This type of grip is used for grasping handles and picking up objects such as mugs. This grip is most effective when the object is shaped such that the hand wraps completely around the object so that the contact area is maximised.

When this grip is used to provide rotational motion, the ease of use depends on the shape of the object and whether frictional contact is required. A handle or lever is the best way to generate rotational motion because it is easy to grip and does not rely on frictional contact.

The most difficult knobs to use are circular, have a hard surface and do not allow the whole hand to be used.

Careful shaping of objects can maximise the effectiveness of a power grip

A knob is frustrating to use if the lock is stiff or the hands are sweaty whereas a handle generates the rotational force more effectively

Dexterity functions: Two-handed tasks

Many tasks with everyday products require the use of both hands at the same time. In some cases this dexterity demand is unnecessary, and an alternative design can allow the product to be used one handed, which will typically reduce design exclusion and increase user satisfaction.

For products that can be used one-handed it is also prudent to cater for those who wish to use the product two-handed. People can suffer from temporary or permanent impairments that reduce the capability of one or both hands, in which case maximum inclusion is obtained when operation of the product is as flexible as possible.

A cordless kettle reduces the dexterity ability required to use it

Remote controls can usually be operated with one or two hands

Environmental context

The ability to perform dexterity tasks that rely on friction can be impaired by the environmental context. A higher strength is required if the hand is sweaty, wet or covered in lubricating substances that are common in workshops or kitchen environments.

Cold temperatures can also affect hand function. The flexibility and sensitivity of the fingers decreases with temperature reducing the dexterity capability. Wearing insulating or protective clothing such as gloves can also make it harder to operate controls on products.

Vibration, motion and the visibility of the hands can also affect the ability to grip or make precision movements. Touch is the only sense that can be employed in low light levels or when the hands and product are not visible.

Dexterity

Kitchen environments contain substances such as fine powders
and oils, which can make controls more difficult to use

Wearing insulating or protective gloves can make
it harder to operate controls on products

Design guidance

- Try to facilitate product interaction that only requires the user to generate pushing forces

- Carefully consider the force and precision requirements for gripping tasks, and ensure that these are appropriate given the size and shape of the surface together with the type of grip that will be used

- Note that controls requiring simultaneous movements in different directions (such as combined pushing and twisting) are particularly difficult for those with reduced motor control

- Enable easier gripping by providing a slightly deformable surface, and maximising the available contact area where possible

- Try to ensure the product can be used left or right handed, and one or two-handed

- Arrange gripping tasks so that they can be performed with the wrist in a neutral and straight position in order to improve user comfort, and minimise pain for those with conditions such as arthritis

- Provide loops, handles or sudden changes in surface contours to help minimise the gripping strength required

- Avoid connection slots that require both vision and dexterity to align

Dexterity

Alternative packaging solutions present different challenges for the user

The phone charger on the left has connection slots that require aligning, while the charger on the right is simpler and easier to insert

Population statistics: Prevalence data

Dexterity ability level (in increasing order)

D1 Cannot pick up and hold a mug of coffee with either hand

D2 Cannot turn a tap or control knobs on a cooker with either hand

D3 Cannot pick up and carry a pint of milk or squeeze the water from a sponge with either hand

D4 Cannot pick up a small object such as a safety pin with either hand

D5 Has difficulty picking up and pouring from a full kettle or serving food from a pan using a spoon or ladle

D6 Has difficulty unscrewing the lid of a coffee jar or using a pen and pencil

D7 Cannot pick up and carry a 5 lb bag of potatoes with either hand

D8 Has difficulty wringing out light washing or using a pair of scissors

D9 Can pick up and hold a mug of tea and coffee with one hand but not with the other

D10 Can turn a tap or control knob with one hand but not with the other. Can squeeze water from a sponge with one hand but not the other

D11 Can pick up a small object such as a safety pin with one hand but not with the other. Can pick up and carry a pint of milk with one hand but not the other. Has difficulty tying a bow in laces or strings

D12 Full dexterity ability

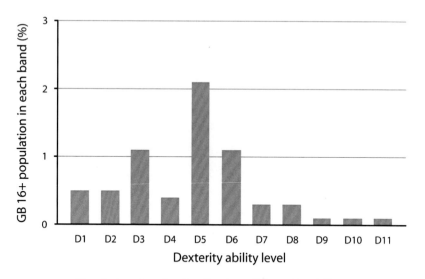

Graph showing the distribution of dexterity ability,
where those with full ability (D12) are not shown

Important note

These ability levels and prevalence statistics are taken
directly from the 1996/97 Disability Follow-up Survey
(Grundy 1999), which was commissioned by the
government to plan welfare support. The GB adult
population was 45.6 million people at the time of the
survey. Please see the Framework section within Part 4:
User capabilities for more detail.

Dexterity

Grundy E, Ahlburg D, Ali M, Breeze E, Sloggett A (1999) Research
report 94 - Disability in Great Britain. Corporate Document Services,
London, UK. ISBN 1-84123-119-3.

Population statistics: Demand & exclusion

No demand

- The user is not required to pick up and carry objects, or perform fine finger manipulation, or grasp objects

Low demand

The user is required to have sufficient ability to do things like

- Perform simple fine finger manipulation with either the left or right hand; e.g. pick up a safety pin
- Pick up and carry a light object with either the left or right hand; e.g. carry a pint of milk
- Grasp an object with either the left or right hand; e.g. squeeze a sponge

Moderate demand

The user is required to have sufficient ability to do things like

- Perform complicated fine finger manipulation with either the left or right hand; e.g. use a pen without difficulty
- Pick up and carry a heavy object with either the left or right hand; e.g. carry a 2.5 kg ($\approx$ 5 lb) bag of potatoes
- Use both hands to grasp something lightly; e.g. unscrew the lid of an instant coffee jar

High demand

The user is required to have sufficient ability to do things like

- Perform two-handed fine finger manipulation; e.g. tie a bow in laces without difficulty
- Pick up and carry a heavy object in each hand; e.g. carry a 2.5 kg ($\approx$ 5 lb) bag of potatoes in each hand
- Grasp an object in each hand; e.g. squeeze a sponge with each hand

Dexterity

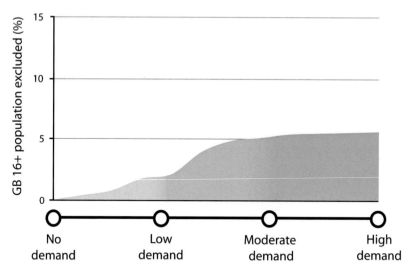

Graph showing the number of people who would be
excluded due to various levels of dexterity demand

Important note

These statements refer to the level of dexterity ability
that a product or service demands, in order to use it.
For a particular demand level, the 1996/97 Disability
Follow-up Survey is used to calculate the total number
of people who do not have this level of ability, and will
therefore be excluded. The GB adult population was
45.6 million people at the time of the survey. Please see
the Framework section within Part 4: User capabilities for
more detail.

Dexterity